North Bullitt High School

D1213491

Childhood
OF FAMOUS AMERICANS

ATHLETES

Babe Didrikson, *de Grummond and Delaune*
Babe Ruth, *Van Riper, Jr.*
Jim Thorpe, *Van Riper, Jr.*
Knute Rockne, *Van Riper, Jr.*
Lou Gehrig, *Van Riper, Jr.*

AUTHORS and COMPOSERS

Ernie Pyle, *Wilson*
Eugene Field, *Borland and Speicher*
Francis Scott Key, *Stevenson*
George Gershwin, *Bryant*
Harriet Beecher Stowe, *Widdemer*
James Fenimore Cooper, *Winders*
James Whitcomb Riley, *Mitchell*
Joel Chandler Harris, *Weddle*
John Philip Sousa, *Weil*
Kate Douglas Wiggin, *Mason*
Katharine Lee Bates, *Myers*
Lew Wallace, *Schaaf*
Louisa Alcott, *Wagoner*
Mark Twain, *Mason*
Mary Mapes Dodge, *Mason*
Noah Webster, *Higgins*
Stephen Foster, *Higgins*
Washington Irving, *Widdemer*

BUSINESSMEN

Allan Pinkerton, *Borland and Speicher*
Andrew Carnegie, *Henry*
A. P. Giannini, *Hammontree*
F. W. Woolworth, *Myers*
John Jacob Astor, *Anderson*
John Wanamaker, *Burt*
Walter Chrysler, *Weddle*

EARLY SETTLERS

James Oglethorpe, *Parks*
John Smith, *Barton*
Myles Standish, *Stevenson*
Peter Stuyvesant, *Widdemer*
Virginia Dare, *Stevenson*
William Bradford, *Smith*
William Penn, *Mason*

ENTERTAINERS

Annie Oakley, *Wilson*
Cecil B. DeMille, *Myers and Burnett*
Ethel Barrymore, *Newman*
Lotta Crabtree, *Place*
P. T. Barnum, *Stevenson*
The Ringling Brothers, *Burt*
Will Rogers, *Van Riper, Jr.*

EXPLORERS and PIONEERS

Amelia Earhart, *Howe*
Brigham Young, *Jordan and Frisbee*
Buffalo Bill, *Stevenson*
Carl Ben Eielson, *Myers and Burnett*
Daniel Boone, *Stevenson*
Davy Crockett, *Parks*
George Rogers Clark, *Wilkie*
Jed Smith, *Burt*
Jim Bowie, *Winders*
Jim Bridger, *Winders*
John Alden, *Burt*
Kit Carson, *Stevenson*
Meriwether Lewis, *Bebenroth*
Narcissa Whitman, *Warner*
Richard Byrd, *Van Riper, Jr.*
Robert Peary, *Clark*
Simon Kenton, *Wilkie*
Vilhjalmur Stefansson, *Myers and Burnett*
Will Clark, *Wilkie*
William Fargo, *Wilkie*
Zeb Pike, *Stevenson*

FOUNDERS of OUR NATION

Alec Hamilton, *Higgins*
Ben Franklin, *Stevenson*
Crispus Attucks, *Millender*
DeWitt Clinton, *Widdemer*
George Washington, *Stevenson*
John Hancock, *Cleven*
John Quincy Adams, *Weil*
Nathan Hale, *Stevenson*
Patrick Henry, *Barton*
Paul Revere, *Stevenson*
Tom Jefferson, *Monsell*

INDIANS

Black Hawk, *Cleven*
Osceola, *Clark*
Pocahontas, *Seymour*
Pontiac, *Peckham*
Sacagawea, *Seymour*
Sequoyah, *Snow*
Sitting Bull, *Stevenson*
Squanto, *Stevenson*
Tecumseh, *Stevenson*

NAVAL HEROES

David Farragut, *Long*
George Dewey, *Long*
John Paul Jones, *Snow*
Matthew Calbraith Perry, *Scharbach*
Oliver Hazard Perry, *Long*
Raphael Semmes, *Snow*
Stephen Decatur, *Smith*

NOTED WIVES and MOTHERS

Abigail Adams, *Wagoner*
Dolly Madison, *Monsell*
Eleanor Roosevelt, *Weil*
Jessie Fremont, *Wagoner*
Martha Washington, *Wagoner*
Mary Todd Lincoln, *Wilkie*
Nancy Hanks, *Stevenson*
Rachel Jackson, *Govan*

SCIENTISTS and INVENTORS

Abner Doubleday, *Dunham*
Albert Einstein, *Hammontree*
Aleck Bell, *Widdemer*
Cyrus McCormick, *Dobler*
Eli Whitney, *Snow*
Elias Howe, *Corcoran*
Elizabeth Blackwell, *Henry*
Gail Borden, *Paradis*
George Carver, *Stevenson*
George Eastman, *Henry*
George Pullman, *Myers*
George Westinghouse, *Dunham*
Henry Ford, *Aird and Ruddiman*
John Audubon, *Mason*
John Burroughs, *Frisbee*
John Deere, *Bare*
John Fitch, *Stevenson*
Lee DeForest, *Dobler*
Luther Burbank, *Burt*
Maria Mitchell, *Melin*
Robert Fulton, *Henry*
Robert Goddard, *Moore*
Samuel Morse, *Snow*
Tom Edison, *Guthridge*
Walter Reed, *Higgins*
Wilbur and Orville Wright, *Stevenson*
Will and Charlie Mayo, *Hammontree*

SOCIAL and CIVIC LEADERS

Betsy Ross, *Weil*
Booker T. Washington, *Stevenson*
Clara Barton, *Stevenson*
Dan Beard, *Mason*
Dorothea Dix, *Melin*
Frances Willard, *Mason*
J. Sterling Morton, *Moore*
Jane Addams, *Wagoner*
John Peter Zenger, Long
Julia Ward Howe, *Wagoner*
Juliette Low, *Higgins*
Liliuokalani, *Newman*
Lucretia Mott, *Burnett*
Molly Pitcher, *Stevenson*
Oliver Wendell Holmes, Jr., *Dunham*
Susan Anthony, *Monsell*

SOLDIERS

Anthony Wayne, *Stevenson*
Bedford Forrest, *Parks*
Dan Morgan, *Bryant*
Douglas MacArthur, *Long*
Ethan Allen, *Winders*
Francis Marion, *Steele*
George Custer, *Stevenson*
Israel Putnam, *Stevenson*
Jeb Stuart, *Winders*
Nathanael Greene, *Peckham*
Robert E. Lee, *Monsell*
Sam Houston, *Stevenson*
Tom Jackson, *Monsell*
U. S. Grant, *Stevenson*
William Henry Harrison, *Peckham*
Zack Taylor, *Wilkie*

STATESMEN

Abe Lincoln, *Stevenson*
Andy Jackson, *Stevenson*
Dan Webster, *Smith*
Franklin Roosevelt, *Weil*
Henry Clay, *Monsell*
Herbert Hoover, *Comfort*
James Monroe, *Widdemer*
Jeff Davis, *de Grummond and Delaune*
John F. Kennedy, *Frisbee*
John Marshall, *Monsell*
Teddy Roosevelt, *Parks*
Woodrow Wilson, *Monsell*

John D. Rockefeller

Boy Financier

Illustrated by Al Fiorentino

John D. Rockefeller

Boy Financier

By Elisabeth P. Myers

THE BOBBS-MERRILL COMPANY, INC.
A SUBSIDIARY OF HOWARD W. SAMS & CO., INC.
Publishers • INDIANAPOLIS • NEW YORK

LIBRARY OF CONGRESS CATALOG CARD NUMBER: 72-11687

PRINTED IN THE UNITED STATES OF AMERICA

To the children who have written me
after reading my books

Illustrations

Full pages

Contents

★ ★ ★

Books by Elisabeth P. Myers

DAVID SARNOFF: RADIO AND TV BOY
EDWARD BOK: YOUNG EDITOR
F. W. WOOLWORTH: FIVE AND TEN BOY
FREDERICK DOUGLASS: BOY CHAMPION OF HUMAN RIGHTS
GEORGE PULLMAN: YOUNG SLEEPING CAR BUILDER
JOHN D. ROCKEFELLER: BOY FINANCIER
KATHARINE LEE BATES: GIRL POET

★ ★ # John D. Rockefeller

Boy Financier

Fresh Apple Pie

COLD WEATHER had come early to upstate New York in the fall of 1843. One morning four-year-old Johnny Rockefeller climbed upon a stool beneath a frost-covered sitting room window. He blew at the frost on the window to melt a peephole to see through. Then he peered out at the bleak November landscape.

"Do you see anything special out there, Johnny?" asked his six-year-old sister Lucy.

"No," replied Johnny. "I just don't see anything special at all."

"Well, then, I guess you might as well come and listen while I read to you," said Lucy.

Lucy's only book was an English grammar, *The Young Lady's Accidence,* which was filled with verses set to rhyme. She had read these verses so often to Johnny that he could recite most of them by himself. Today as she read the following lines, he said them along with her:

"A letter is an uncompounded sound
Of which there no division can be found.
Those sounds to certain characters we fix
Which in the English tongue are twenty-six."

When Lucy finished reading this verse, Johnny went right on to the first line of the second verse without waiting for her read:

" 'A' was an Archer who shot at a frog—"

Johnny was supposed to wait for Mary to read. His going on like this made her angry. "Mama," she shouted, "Johnny is misbehaving!"

Johnny whirled on his stool. "I am not!" he protested vigorously.

Their mother, Eliza Rockefeller, came hurrying in from the next room with their two-and-a-half-year-old brother William clinging to her skirt. Sternly she looked at them and quoted one of her favorite pieces of poetry:

"Birds in their little nests agree;
And 'tis a shameful sight
When children in one family
Fall out and chide and fight."

Lucy and Johnny both realized that their mother was scolding them and hung their heads in shame. "Now kiss and make up," she said soothingly. At once they jumped down from their chairs and pecked each other's cheeks.

The Rockefeller family lived in a small frame cottage near Richford, New York. Eliza's husband, William Avery Rockefeller, was a big jovial person whom everybody called Big Bill. Many other Rockefellers lived nearby, including Big Bill's father, Godfrey Rockefeller, and several of his brothers and sisters.

Eliza was the daughter of a prosperous farmer named John Davison, who lived near Batavia, about forty miles away. After Big Bill had married her, he had brought her to this community to live near his relatives. Then when her first son was born, she had named him John Davison after her father.

Most of the time Eliza lived alone with her children. Big Bill went away on long trips, lasting many months, sometimes even a year or two. At present he had been gone ever since soon after William had been born.

Everybody was curious about Big Bill's long trips. He explained that he was a salesman, but nobody, not even Eliza, knew what he sold. Whenever he returned home, however, he always seemed to have plenty of money. He paid up his bills and left money with Eliza to help support the family until he came home again.

Eliza bought only things that she actually

needed at the grocery store in Richford. Often the storekeeper said to her, "Don't stint yourself. Big Bill told me to let you have whatever you need while he is away. He has always paid me before, and I know that he'll pay me this time when he returns."

Eliza had been taught by her frugal Scotch father, John Davison, to be frugal herself. Often when the storekeeper urged her to buy something, she said, "I don't want to be any more beholden to you than necessary."

Today after Lucy finished reading to Johnny, their mother said, "Now you may help me to bake a fresh apple pie."

Johnny clapped his hands. He liked apple pie more than almost anything else. "Oh, good!" he cried. "I can hardly wait."

There were apple trees around the Rockefeller cottage, and each fall Eliza gathered apples to store away in the cellar. She used them chiefly to bake pies for the children. She never baked more than one pie at a time, because she kept very little sugar in the house.

Promptly Lucy and Johnny started to help their mother. Johnny offered to go to the cellar to get the apples for the pie. His mother, realizing that it was dangerous for him to go to the dark cellar alone, handed a lighted candle to Lucy. "Here, Lucy," she said. "Go along and hold this candle for him so he can see what he is doing. Be careful on the steps."

Eliza depended on candles for lighting her home. She made most of the candles out of tallow, or animal fat, instead of buying candles at the store. They didn't last long, but they cost much less than ready-made candles.

Both Johnny and Lucy carefully climbed down the steps into the dark cellar. Then Lucy held up the candle while Johnny took down a large crock of apples from a shelf. "Now you go ahead to light the way with the candle and I'll follow you back up the steps," he said.

Lucy started to climb the steps, but by now the candle was burning low and gave very little light. "Hurry, Johnny," she called. "The candle is starting to go out."

While Lucy was talking, the candle went out completely. Johnny knew the way, however, and cautiously climbed back up the steps, carrying the crock of apples. "Thank you, Johnny," said his mother. "Now wash your hands so you can help with the dough."

Johnny washed his hands in the kitchen sink and stepped onto the back porch to wipe them on a towel. The wind outside was blowing bitterly cold and he stepped back inside as soon as possible. "This is not a fit day to be outdoors," he said.

By now his mother had rolled out flat dough for the bottom and top crusts of the pie. She placed the dough for the bottom crust into a pie pan. Then Johnny pressed it tightly to the bottom and sides of the pan. At the same time Lucy mixed apples, sugar, and cinnamon for the filling of the pie.

Finally Eliza poured the mixture into the dough which Johnny had pressed to the bottom and sides of the pie pan. "May I have a taste of it before you cover it?" he asked.

"Yes, since Lucy has already had a taste, you may have one, too," said his mother.

Lucy's face turned red. "But how did you know that I had a taste?" she asked.

"There are telltale signs on your mouth," her mother replied.

A few minutes later Johnny climbed up to the frost-covered window again. He cleaned away the frost from the spot which he had cleaned before. This time when he looked out he saw a horse and buggy coming up the lane toward the house. Excitedly he called, "Mama, someone is coming to see us."

At once Eliza came to look out the clear spot on the window. "Let me see," she said. "Maybe your father is coming home."

Moments later Eliza recognized the man in the buggy as her husband. "Yes," she cried, "that's your father coming! Wait here while I go outside to meet him."

Eliza rushed out just as her husband brought the buggy to a stop. "Bill!" she called. "Welcome home!"

Big Bill tossed the lines aside and jumped down from the buggy. He stopped to kiss Eliza and took her into his arms. Then, talking and laughing, he carried her into the house.

Inside the house Big Bill put Eliza down, but they kept on talking. Finally with a joyous laugh, Eliza twisted away from him and said, "Don't forget the children."

"Oh, no, I won't!" he said.

Happily he sat down in a chair and asked both Lucy and Johnny to come to him. Moments later he kissed them and took them on his lap.

Then he started to talk with them and they relaxed contentedly on his knees.

He told them interesting stories about animals which he had seen on his trip, including several bears. He told them about Indians whom he had seen from time to time. Suddenly he reached in his pockets and pulled out some trinkets which he had obtained from Indians.

"Oh, how wonderful!" cried the children as they leaned back against him to examine the trinkets. "We surely wish you could come home more often to see us," they added.

Eliza had been watching. "I see you still have all your old charm," she said, laughing.

"I hope so," said her husband. "Now I wonder if I can use it to get something to eat."

At the mention of something to eat, Johnny sat upright and said, "Oh, yes, you're sure to have something wonderful to eat. You're going to have fresh apple pie!"

A Cayuga Indian

BIG BILL Rockefeller made everybody happy by coming home. As usual he had plenty of money, even though nobody knew how he had earned it. He settled all his bills, bought all members of the family new clothes, and still had some money left. Johnny knew, because he saw a wad of greenbacks in his father's wallet.

Often that winter Johnny went to the village of Richford with his father. He liked to see the broad village green or central park, which now was covered with snow. He liked to hear the jolly voices of the lumbermen, who gathered around the stove at the village store. He was especially proud when they begged his father to tell them about his traveling experiences.

As Johnny listened, he came to believe that his father had traveled almost everywhere. He related exciting experiences which he had had with people, always including a few which he had had with Indians.

Besides relating stories about his travels, Big Bill often made prophecies about the future of America. "The era of horses is almost gone," he said. "Now that we have steam engines, we won't need horses much longer."

This prophecy brought shouts of laughter from the group of listeners. Most of them realized that steam was becoming an important source of power. Even so, they were so accustomed to using horses that they couldn't realize trying to get along without them.

One evening that winter while Big Bill was still at home, he and Eliza discussed moving to Cayuga County, where her parents lived. Johnny listened closely to their conversation, because he knew that Cayuga was the home of the Cayuga Indians. Already his father had told him interesting stories about them.

The conversation went on for a couple of hours. Finally Big Bill said, "As you know, I like Cayuga County. It was my stomping ground when I courted you, but your father has never forgiven me for taking you away."

Eliza took out a handkerchief from her apron pocket and wiped her eyes. "Yes, I know," she said, "but he surely will forgive you when he sees his little namesake here," she said.

Big Bill winked at Johnny. "Your mother's referring to you," he said. "Do you think you can melt your grandfather's icy heart?"

Johnny sat quietly for a few moments, puzzled by this conversation. He knew that his mother never went to visit his grandfather and that his grandfather never came to visit her. Finally he replied, "I don't know."

His father chuckled. "Well, we'll just have to wait and see," he said. "Anyhow, when we have a good spell of weather, you and I will go to Cayuga County to look for a new home."

Johnny could scarcely believe his ears. He clapped his hands and cried, "Oh, good!"

For several months, Johnny kept watching the weather. Finally in March, 1844, some of the ice and snow began to disappear. "Now is the weather good enough for us to go to Cayuga County?" he asked.

Big Bill rumpled Johnny's sandy hair affectionately with his hand and said, "You surely don't forget anything, do you?"

"Not if it's important," said Johnny.

"All right," said his father. "We'll leave for Cayuga County tomorrow morning. Ask your mother to pack you a bundle of clothes."

That night Johnny was far too excited to sleep. Never before had he been farther from home than the village of Richford. Now he was going forty or more miles away and would have many interesting stories to tell Lucy when he returned home.

The next morning after breakfast Big Bill and Johnny climbed into the buggy and started to drive away. A few minutes later Johnny asked, "Will we see any Indians on our trip?"

Big Bill looked doubtful. "I'm not sure," he replied. "Indians are becoming harder to find these days."

"Oh," said Johnny sadly. "Well, I surely hope we find some."

"Maybe we will," said his father consolingly, "but we'll have to keep looking."

They drove along roads that led through hilly wooded country and crossed numerous small ice-covered streams. Occasionally they spotted a wild turkey or a deer scooting away to seek shelter among the trees. "There's plenty of game in these woods and plenty of fish in the streams," said Big Bill.

At the end of the second day away from home, they came to the village of Moravia. Big Bill drove up to the front door of the hotel and said, "We'll stay here tonight."

That evening Big Bill sat in the lobby of the hotel and visited with the other guests. Johnny, trying to keep awake, sat nearby and listened drowsily. Soon he heard his father say, "My son has been hoping that we would see some Indians on our trip."

At once Johnny was wide awake. He jumped up and exclaimed, "And I'm still hoping."

"Maybe we can help you," said one of the guests, "but don't speak so loudly."

Johnny clapped one of his hands over his mouth. Then his father motioned toward a man sleeping on a bench a short distance away. "According to these men, that man is a Cayuga Indian," he said softly.

Johnny stared in surprise. The man asleep on the bench didn't look like an Indian. Instead he was dressed like a lumberjack with a plaid shirt and woolen leggings. "I can't believe he's an Indian," said Johnny doubtfully.

"Well, he's both an Indian and a lumberjack," said the man who had spoken before.

Curiously Johnny tiptoed toward the bench with his father following a few steps behind. The Indian sat up and Johnny wanted to run, but his feet seemed rooted to the floor. Then the Indian smiled broadly and held out his hand. "Come here, boy," he said in a friendly tone of voice.

Johnny still was frightened, but he inched forward and gingerly accepted the Indian's extended hand. The Indian gave a grunt of

approval and drew him to the bench beside him. "You are a brave little boy," he said.

By now Johnny's heart was pounding. He looked around for his father, who now had rejoined the other guests. Finally he managed to ask, "Are you really an Indian?"

"Yes, I'm a Cayuga and proud to be one," replied the Indian. "The Cayugas are part of a six-nation Confederation founded more than two hundred years ago by Hiawatha. This great Mohawk chief wanted us to live under our own laws and to worship the Great Spirit in our own way. When the white men came, they took over our lands and even our own rights."

The Indian sounded so grieved that Johnny was eager to comfort him. "I guess they forgot the Golden Rule: 'Do unto others as you would have them do unto you,'" he said soberly. "Mama says that this would be a much better world if people would only live by this rule."

"But people won't," said the Indian. "That's one reason why I'm glad to be a Cayuga, which means a 'person of superior cunning.' Do you know what it means to be cunning?"

Johnny shook his head. "Not exactly," he said, "only I know some animals are cunning."

"Well, it means you always should keep your wits sharp," explained the Indian, "and never let anyone catch you napping."

"Just as I didn't catch you," said Johnny.

"That's right," said the Indian.

Briefly they sat silently side by side. Then Johnny slid off the bench to return to his father. "Thank you," he called to the Indian. "From now on I'll try to be cunning."

The Indian chuckled. "I hope so," he said.

Johnny walked slowly back to his father. Big Bill arose smilingly and led the way to their bedroom. "Well, do you feel any better now that you have met an Indian?" he inquired.

"Oh, yes, I surely do," replied Johnny. "I'll never forget meeting him."

The next day Big Bill and Johnny went to look for a new family home. Only three miles from Moravia, they came to a beautiful house on a hill overlooking Lake Owasco. "I think your mother will like this spot," said Big Bill. "There are neighbors close by and her father lives on the other side of the lake."

"I'm sure she will," said Johnny. "And I'll like it too, only we won't have apple trees here and I won't have any apple pies."

The Conestoga Wagon

After Big Bill and Johnny returned from selecting a new home near Moravia, the family immediately prepared to move. Big Bill was eager to leave at the earliest possible moment. "There is no need to wait," he said.

He bought a big Conestoga wagon for hauling the family belongings. Eliza objected and said, "Bill, we don't need anything so grand just for hauling our things."

"Well, we might as well be comfortable and have plenty of room for taking everything," replied Big Bill. "Besides, I might want to use the wagon for something later."

"I can't imagine what for," said Eliza.

The new Conestoga wagon was colored like the American flag. The body was bright red, the canvas cover was dazzling white, and the wheels and under parts were sparkling blue. The front wheels were taller than Johnny and the back wheels were taller than his mother. Both Johnny and Lucy thought the new wagon was gorgeous. Johnny climbed up on the driver's bench and pretended to be driving.

"Where are we going to get horses to pull this big wagon?" asked Eliza. "Our two horses certainly can't pull it."

"I've contracted for two regular Conestoga horses," replied Big Bill. "They'll be much stronger than ordinary horses."

Johnny knew exactly what these Conestoga horses would be like. Occasionally he had seen several teams of Conestoga horses resting in the village of Richford. They were big powerful creatures with broad backs, short arched necks, and stout, springy legs. A driver had to be very alert to manage them.

Eliza let Johnny play at driving only a few minutes. "Come down," she called to him. "We need you to help."

The work of dismantling the house took over half a day. Everything had to be stowed carefully in the wagon and anchored to keep it from sliding. One bed had to be set up inside for sleeping purposes. Big Bill said that Eliza, Lucy, and William would sleep in this bed. "Johnny and I will sleep where men who drive wagons usually sleep," he added.

"Where's that?" Johnny asked excitedly.

"On the ground under the wagon," explained his father, much to Johnny's surprise.

During the first day of the trip, Johnny continuously wondered what it would be like to sleep beneath the wagon. That night when he watched his mother and Lucy and William crawl into bed inside the wagon, he almost wished that he could crawl in, too.

His father spread out a big piece of canvas and two thick blankets on the ground under the wagon. "Now watch as I roll myself up in one of the blankets," he said. "Then you'll know how to roll up in the other blanket."

Big Bill lay down across a corner of one of the blankets and rolled to wrap himself up tightly. Johnny looked at him and giggled. "You look like you're inside a cocoon," he cried.

"Yes, you might say that I look like a bug in a rug," said Big Bill in return.

"Well, I'll try to be a bug, too," said Johnny, starting to roll himself up.

"Now go to sleep at once," said his father. "Tomorrow will be another busy day."

Big Bill, following his own advice, went to sleep immediately. Johnny closed his eyes and tried to do the same, but he felt strangely alone lying there wide awake in the dark.

Moments later he began to hear all sorts of unusual noises. He wondered whether any of them came from bears or panthers roaming about. What if they became curious about the wagon? Would it be possible to escape?

He held his breath in order to listen better. Then he found that he could identify some of the sounds. He recognized the mournful hooting of an owl in the distance and the sleepy chirping of birds nearby. He heard his father's horses occasionally stamp their feet.

Now he felt safer. He had heard that horses could smell danger. Undoubtedly they would raise a ruckus if a bear or panther came near. He reached out, put one hand on his father's blanket, and went sound asleep.

The next day the Rockefellers continued their journey. When evening came, they were only a

few miles from Moravia. Big Bill wanted to keep on going until they reached their new home, but Eliza objected. "We'll be better off to stop along the way," she said, "because we won't have any furniture in the house."

This second night Johnny thoroughly enjoyed sleeping beside his father under the wagon. "I only wish that we were going farther so I could sleep out some more," he said.

Soon after the Rockefellers moved to their new home, Johnny reached his fifth birthday. He felt thankful because his father was home to help him celebrate. On previous birthdays his mother usually had baked him something tasty to eat and given him something new to wear. This year he hoped to get something more exciting for his birthday.

He obtained his wish. Big Bill handed him a new rifle and said, "Now after you learn to shoot, you can go hunting with the men."

Johnny had plenty of time to learn to shoot because the men round-about did little hunting in the summer. Most of them were too busy raising crops on their farms. Big Bill hired a man to raise the crops on his farm. "I'm a salesman, not a farmer," he said.

During the summer Big Bill taught Johnny many sports. He taught him how to shoot his new rifle, how to ride a horse, how to swim, and how to row a boat. Johnny was very proud to be able to do all these special things.

Later in the summer Big Bill prepared to leave on a trip in the big Conestoga wagon. At once neighbors became curious, wondering where he was going and what he planned to do. They wondered, too, how he obtained all the money which he seemed to have in his pockets. Finally some of them asked Eliza, and she reported it to Big Bill. "The neighbors don't understand why you are so secretive," she said. "They wonder why you don't tell them where you are going and what you are going to do."

Big Bill's eyes flashed in anger. "They've no right to ask," he replied. "So long as I'm not ashamed of where I'm going or what I'm going to do, I don't care what they think."

Johnny had been waiting nearby during this conversation. Suddenly Big Bill turned to him and added, "Remember what I just said. So long as you're not ashamed of where you are going or what you are doing, you don't need to worry about what people think."

The Man of the House

In mid-August, 1844, a new baby girl named Mary Ann joined the Rockefeller family. Shortly after her birth, Big Bill announced that he would leave on another business trip.

"Will you be gone long?" asked Eliza.

"Maybe yes and maybe no," he replied. "All will depend on how I find business."

Later that day Big Bill bade all the members of his family good-by. When he came to Johnny he said, "Johnny, you're to be the man of the house until I come back. I'll count on you to take care of everybody while I'm away."

"I will," said Johnny soberly.

Johnny had enjoyed being with his father and hoped that he would stay away only a few weeks. That fall he began to watch closely for Big Bill's Conestoga wagon to come up the drive. Often his heart leaped with hope, because many Conestoga wagons traveled along the road in front of the house. Both fall and winter passed, however, and still Big Bill hadn't returned.

The following spring Eliza began to run out of money for the family living expenses. At last seven-year-old Lucy took Johnny aside for a heart-to-heart talk about their mother. "Mama's worried about money," she said, "and I wish we could earn some to help her out."

Johnny remembered the important responsibility his father had given him. He stiffened his five-and-a-half-year-old shoulders and said, "Leave it to me, Lucy. I'll go to the neighbors and ask to work for them to earn money."

Johnny was rather tall for his age, but skinny to the point of looking scrawny. His grandfather Davison once had teased him about resembling a picked chicken. "As skinny as you are, any self-respecting fox would think twice before eating you," he had said.

The Rockefellers' neighbors seemed to share this feeling about Johnny. They looked at him in surprise when he asked them for work. "Come back in a year or so after you become larger and stronger," they said.

Finally Johnny had visited all the neighbors except one. This one neighbor was a farmer named Caleb Skinner. Most people called him "Old Skinflint" because he had a reputation of being miserly in all his dealings.

As Johnny trudged along the road to Mr. Skinner's farm, he didn't feel very hopeful about finding work. When he walked up the path to the house, however, he noted that the family garden was littered with small stones which winter freezing had pushed up from the ground. These stones would have to be cleared away before the garden could be plowed and planted.

Much to Johnny's surprise, when he knocked on the back door, Mr. Skinner stuck out his head. "I saw you coming," he said. "Who are you and what do you want?"

Johnny snatched off his cap. "I'm John Davison Rockefeller," he said, "and I would like to work for you. Will you hire me to pick up the stones in your garden?"

Mr. Skinner looked down at Johnny. "So you're John Davison Rockefeller?" he said. "Well, I've heard of you and I know your grandfather, John Davison. He's a properous farmer and you look like a chip off the same block. Come on in and have something to eat."

When Johnny entered the house, Mrs. Skinner was standing beside the kitchen stove stirring a pan of oatmeal. Her husband turned to her and said, "Miranda, this is young John Davison Rockefeller. Ladle out a bowlful of oatmeal for him. Being a Scotsman, he must like porridge."

Mrs. Skinner placed a bowl of oatmeal, a bowl of brown sugar, and a pitcher of cream on the table. "Now sit down and eat," she said. Johnny needed no urging, because he was both hungry and tired from walking.

While Johnny was eating, Mr. Skinner sat down beside him. "I hear that your father is gone from home most of the time in his big Conestoga wagon," he said. "He certainly isn't much like your grandfather. He's a big spender, but your grandfather is a penny-pincher."

"Caleb," scolded Mrs. Skinner. "You shouldn't say such things to the lad."

Mr. Skinner ignored his wife's scolding and kept right on talking with Johnny. "Well, pinching pennies seems to pay off because your grandfather is a well-to-do man," he said. "Do you think that you are going to take after him?"

"I don't know," replied Johnny. "I'd like to be rich, but I've never had any pennies to pinch." Then he remembered why he had come and added, "Maybe I can earn some if you'll let me pick up the stones in your garden."

Mr. Skinner hesitated, but his wife said, "Let him pick up the stones. We'll have to get rid of them before planting."

"I didn't say I wouldn't," said Mr. Skinner. "As a matter of fact, I will."

Johnny beamed at him. "I'll start as soon as I finish my porridge," he said.

Mrs. Skinner put a gentle hand on his shoulder. "Don't hurry," she said. "Just come back tomorrow to pick up the stones."

Johnny could hardly wait to tell Lucy he had a job. He made a sign to her to meet him in the parlor, where they could talk alone. "Good," she said. "Now you'll need a secret place to hide the pennies you earn."

They looked all about the parlor for a good place to hide the pennies. Finally they chose a beautiful blue bowl which rested on top of a small chest of drawers. "Nobody will find them in this bowl," said Johnny.

Johnny worked two full days picking up the stones in the Skinner garden. He carried them to the edges of the garden and made a stone border round about. Mrs. Skinner liked the border which Johnny built, but Mr. Skinner scoffed at the idea. "His building that border was just a waste of time," he grumbled. "He could have finished his work much sooner by wheeling the stones away."

"But he was too small to use a wheelbarrow," argued Mrs. Skinner. "He couldn't possibly have wheeled the stones away."

Slowly Mr. Skinner reached in his pocket and pulled out a scuffed leather purse. He opened it, picked out two shillings, and handed them to Johnny. "Here's your pay for picking up the stones," he said, "but not for the time you wasted in building that border."

Johnny's eyes glowed as he looked at the two shillings. He didn't know much about money, but realized that each shilling was worth a goodly number of pennies. Immediately he decided to take the shillings to the bank in Moravia and trade them for pennies. He could hardly wait to get home to put the pennies in the blue bowl. "Thank you, Mr. Skinflint!" he called back without thinking.

Mrs. Skinner looked at her husband and began to laugh. "That serves you right, Caleb, for pinching pennies," she exclaimed.

Happy Times with Big Bill

BIG BILL returned home in May in a very jovial mood. "Business has been good, so I've decided to take a few months off," he said. "What's going on around here of interest to me?"

"Well, the people are preparing to put up a new schoolhouse," replied Eliza. "I hope they'll locate it near here, so it will be handy for Johnny and Lucy."

"I hope so, too," said Big Bill. "Then they won't have far to walk in winter storms and blizzards. While I'm home, I'll see what I can do about the matter."

The next morning Big Bill carefully saddled

two horses, and he and Johnny rode into town. Johnny felt very proud as he rode beside his father. When they reached town, they pulled up in front of the bank. "Go inside and ask the banker to come out to help me," said Big Bill.

Johnny jumped down from his horse and went inside. The only other time he had ever been in the bank was when he had stopped to exchange his two shillings for pennies. The banker recognized him and asked, "What can I do for you, young Mr. Rockefeller?"

Johnny grinned at being greeted as if he were grown up. "My father is outside," he replied, "and he wants you to come to help him."

The banker came out from behind the counter and walked outside with Johnny. He shook hands with Big Bill and asked, "Did you hit the jackpot on this trip?"

"Yes, in a way," replied Big Bill.

Big Bill took several pouches of money from

his saddlebags and handed them to the banker. They were so heavy that the banker had trouble handling them. "You're lucky that you weren't waylaid by bandits," he said.

Big Bill laughed. "The way I travel nobody would suspect that I have a red cent," he said. He took out other pouches of money and followed the banker toward the door. Then suddenly he turned and called to Johnny, "You stay with the horses. I won't be gone long."

While Johnny was waiting, he wondered how his father had obtained the big bags of money. At last he decided to ask him. "How did you earn all that money?" he asked when Big Bill returned to the wagon.

In reply Big Bill merely rumpled Johnny's hair. "That's my secret," he said. "You're too young to understand now, but later you'll learn to keep some things secret, too."

Johnny frowned, wondering what his father

meant by this statement. Big Bill quickly changed the subject by saying, "Now let's drop in at the General Store."

Johnny's face cleared. "Oh, good!" he said.

The General Store was located in a two-story frame building with a porch in front. On both sides of the front door there were benches where people could sit and visit, if the weather permitted. When Big Bill and Johnny reached the store, the two benches were filled. Several persons arose to shake hands with Big Bill and said, "We heard you were back."

There was a bulletin board on the front door of the store. People posted all sorts of notices and announcements there. Some told of elections to take place and farm auctions to be held. Some invited people to join hunting parties and to attend church socials. Others announced births and deaths in the neighborhood.

Big Bill and Johnny stopped to read the notices and announcements. By now Johnny could read them fairly well, thanks to his mother's tutoring. "This bulletin board is as good as a newspaper," said his father.

Soon they stepped inside the store. Johnny looked about eagerly because he hadn't been there for some time. The walls on both sides of the store were lined with shelves, bins, and drawers filled with a variety of things to sell. Out from the walls stretched long flat counters and show cases. At the rear were stacks of tools, such as hoes, rakes, scythes, and axes. Hanging from the rear wall were kitchen utensils, such as kettles, pails, and pans.

Johnny liked the good odors from foods in the store. He and his father sauntered about until they came to a pickle barrel near the cash register. The storekeeper pointed to the barrel and said jovially to Johnny, "Help yourself, but be careful not to fall in."

Big Bill and the storekeeper talked while Johnny climbed up on a box beside the barrel. He reached down and tried to grab one of the pickles floating about loosely in the brine. At last he succeeded and felt as if he had hooked a fish. Then he took a big crunchy bite and climbed down to walk on with his father.

Before long they came to a section of toys and games. There were checkerboards, wagons, sleds, dolls, and many other things on display. Johnny stopped to examine a little bank, which was shaped like a bear. "Would you like to have that bank?" asked his father.

Johnny's eyes shone with delight. "Yes," he replied. "Then I won't have to save pennies in that blue bowl any longer."

Big Bill told the storekeeper that he wished to purchase the bank for Johnny. "Good," said the storekeeper. "A boy can't start too early in life, learning to save money."

On the way home Big Bill said to Johnny, "This has been a good morning in town. I have deposited my money in the bank and offered to find a central location for the new schoolhouse."

"I don't understand what you mean by a central location," said Johnny.

"Well, you'll find out when the time comes," said his father.

Eliza was pleased when Big Bill told her about his offer to locate the new schoolhouse. She was happy to have him take an interest in community affairs, because it would help people to realize that he was a responsible citizen and good family man.

About this time, Big Bill decided to sell timber from some of the woods on the farm. He hired several lumberjacks, or woodmen, to cut down trees and to drag the logs to the lake.

Later they would lash the logs together to make a raft and float them to a sawmill. Johnny was fascinated with the lumberjacks because they often sang as they worked. He especially liked what he called their "Alphabet Song," with such lines as the following:

E is for echo that through the woods rang,
F for the foreman who bosseth the gang;
G is for grindstone, so swift it did turn,
H is for handle, so smooth it was worn.

When the lumberjacks finished their work, Johnny was very sorry to have them leave. He wished that he could float away with them to watch the sawmill cut the logs into lumber. Big Bill, on the other hand, was happy because now he had some additional money.

After the woodmen left, Johnny often sang the alphabet song. One day when he was outdoors singing, his father interrupted him as he came to these lines:

O for the owl that hooteth by night.
P for the pine that always fell right.

"Your singing that alphabet song reminded me that I'm supposed to find a central location for the new schoolhouse," he said. "Run into the house and tell your mother that we're going to find the location now."

Johnny ran fast into the house and soon came back again grinning. "Mama says to tell you to locate the schoolhouse as close to our house as possible," he said.

Big Bill chuckled. "I'll do my very best," he said.

He drove horses hitched to a wagon across the school district from north to south and from east to west, counting the number of times one of the front wheels turned around. Then he drove over the same routes again until the wheel had turned around only half the first number of times. "Well, this is the central location," he said, coming to a halt.

Johnny looked and noticed that the location

was very close to the Rockefeller home. "This location is fine for us," he said. "Mama surely will be pleased."

"Yes," said Big Bill. "We'll live closer to the schoolhouse than anybody else. Maybe your mother will want the teacher to stay with her while I'm away on my next trip."

As Big Bill mentioned going away again, Johnny felt a big lump in his throat. "Do you have to go?" he asked.

"Of course," said his father. "I can't stay on vacation forever, but I won't leave for a couple of months. Don't say anything to your mother about my going."

Johnny swallowed hard. "I won't say a word to her about it," he promised.

Smarter Than a Turkey

THE NEW schoolhouse at Moravia was built out of logs. The men from the neighborhood donated their services to put up the building. First they cleared off the site and drove stakes to show where the building would stand. Big Bill was still around to help with the work.

The women and children kept busy nearby while the men worked. The women prepared food for the men to eat, and the children toted buckets of water for them to drink. The entire affair, which lasted several days, was much like a big neighborhood social gathering.

Big Bill urged Johnny to watch the men

closely as they worked. "You may never have a chance to see work of this kind again," he said. "The day for building log cabins in this country is about over."

Johnny watched every move the men made. First they made the floor by placing puncheons side by side with the flat sides up. Next they put up the walls by piling the logs on top of one another, leaving openings for the window and a door. They carefully filled all the spaces between the logs with mud. Last they put up the roof by nailing long board-like pieces of lumber to slender log rafters.

Finally the building was complete except for shutters and a door, which a few men had made while the others had put up the building. These men promptly hung the shutters at the windows and the door at the front opening. Then all the men stood back, looked admiringly at the new building, and gave a shout of joy.

The women had prepared a special banquet for the men on the last day. The men sat at a long table and feasted on all sorts of delicacies. After they finished eating, they continued to sit and visit.

While the men were eating and visiting, the boys roamed off by themselves. Soon some of the older boys started to play mumble-ty-peg. This was a game in which each player tried to toss an open jackknife so that it would land with the blade sticking in the ground and the handle sticking upward. If the player failed in his attempt, he had to kneel and pull a peg from the ground with his teeth.

Johnny and his brother William merely stood and watched the older boys play. Johnny watched curiously because he never had played the game or seen it played before. Finally one of the older boys invited him to join them.

Slowly Johnny shook his head. "I haven't any

knife," he said. He was very thankful because he could readily see that the game required a great deal of skill.

"That's no problem," replied the boy. "We'll lend you a knife."

"Sure," added some of the other boys. "We'll lend you a knife."

At once one of the boys handed Johnny an open jackknife. Johnny, feeling very uneasy, took the open knife and tried to balance it on the palm of his hand. He wondered whether he could flip his wrist in the right way to make the knife land with its blade sticking in the ground and its handle sticking upward. He wished that he could practice tossing it a few times. Finally one of the boys called impatiently, "Well, are you going to play or aren't you?"

Johnny took a deep breath. He knew that he either had to toss the knife or be called a "Fraidy Cat." He had no choice in the matter. Above all, he didn't want the boys to think he was afraid. "I'm going to play," he said.

"Then go ahead," cried the other boys. "We can't wait all afternoon."

Johnny held out the knife and flipped his wrist, but the knife fell flat on the ground. He watched silently as some of the boys drove a peg into the ground. Suddenly he told William to go back to the schoolhouse. He didn't want William to see him being humiliated.

The boys led Johnny to the peg and gathered around to watch him. "Remember that you can't use anything except your lips and teeth to pull out the peg," they said. "Keep your hands clasped tightly behind you."

Just as Johnny was starting to get down on his knees, he noticed his father walking briskly toward the group. Apparently William had reported to him what was happening. Big Bill said nothing, but just stood near and watched.

Now Johnny knew all the more that he must pull out the peg. He gripped his hands behind him and tried again and again to grasp the peg with his teeth, but somehow his nose kept getting in the way. Soon he began to get dust in his eyes and could hardly see the peg. Finally just as he was beginning to feel that he would have to give up, he managed to grab the peg with his teeth.

All the time he had struggled, trying to grab the peg, the boys had grunted to remind him that he was acting like a pig. When he climbed to his feet, holding the peg in his mouth, however, they gave him a rousing cheer. Big Bill cheered along with the others.

The boys told Johnny that he could keep the peg as a souvenir. As he walked away with his father, he was almost as proud and happy as he would have been had he tossed the knife correctly in the first place.

The community leaders employed a young woman, named Sophie Parker, to teach in the new schoolhouse. She lived in another community but arranged to stay with the Rockefellers, since they lived closer to the school than anybody else. Lucy and Johnny were very happy to have her live with them.

In the spring of 1846, Eliza gave birth to twin boys, Frank and Francis. Frank was a healthy baby, but Francis was weak and frail. After Big Bill left on another trip, the school teacher helped to take care of them.

One day a huge flock of wild turkeys roosted in the trees near the Rockefeller house. Quietly Johnny got his rifle and shot one of them. After it fell shrieking to the ground, he rushed to pick it up, but dropped it almost instantly. Somehow as he looked down at its glassy eyes he felt guilty for having taken its life.

He could scarcely bear the thought of touching the turkey again, but he knew that his mother would appreciate having it to cook. At last he mustered up courage to take hold of its feet and carry it into the house. "Here, Mama," he said, "is a wild turkey which I shot."

"Oh, thank you, Johnny!" she exclaimed joyfully. "Now we'll have a real feast this evening." Johnny put a hand over his mouth and rushed out the door. The mere thought of eating the turkey made him feel sick.

That evening his mother served roast turkey with all the trimmings, and everybody ate heartily except Johnny. Afterwards, while he was kneeling beside his bed to say his prayers, he solemnly vowed never to shoot a living creature again. If his mother needed food for the table, he'd try to secure it in some other way.

The next day the huge flock of turkeys disappeared. Some drovers came along and shooed the turkeys away to the market place. "That's something your father could have done, if he had been here," Eliza said to Johnny. "There's good money in turkeys."

Johnny noted the wistfulness in his mother's voice and was troubled. A few days later, early in the morning, he happened to see a turkey hen stalking near the edge of the woods. She evidently had been left behind when the drovers had chased the other turkeys away.

Johnny watched the turkey hen for a few moments. She moved cautiously and shifted her head from side to side, as if she were afraid of something. "She probably has a brood of baby turkeys hidden somewhere," explained Eliza, who had come out to watch, too.

"I'd like to see them," said Johnny.

"That will be hard to do, because the hen will try to keep you from finding them," replied his mother. "If you find them, however, you might bring them back and raise them."

This idea appealed to Johnny. He knew that some of the baby turkeys in the brood were almost certain to die or to be eaten by bloodthirsty animals. Possibly, if he could find them, he could save most of them. If he could only save one of them, his conscience wouldn't hurt him so much for having killed a turkey. "I'm going to try," he said.

"Good luck," said his mother.

Johnny tried not to let the turkey hen know he was shadowing her. He kept upwind of her to keep her from smelling him, a trick that he had learned from his father. Nevertheless, when night came, he still hadn't found the brood of baby turkeys. "Don't feel discouraged," said his mother. "Many people have failed in trying to find a wild turkey's nest."

"I'm just mad at myself more than anything else," said Johnny, shaking his head. "I surely ought to be smarter than a turkey!"

It took Johnny two more full days to locate the brood of baby turkeys. The turkey hen took numerous angry nips at him, attempting to drive him away. Finally, however, he succeeded in putting the baby turkeys into a basket and carrying them home to raise.

During the coming weeks and months Johnny took good care of the baby turkeys and watched them grow. Finally he sold some of them but kept others to start a flock of turkeys. Then from time to time when he sold additional turkeys he put money in the little bear bank which his father had bought for him.

Often Johnny took money from his bear bank and deposited it in the bank in Moravia. "You're piling up a real stake for yourself, young Rockefeller," said the banker admiringly. "What's the secret of your success?"

"Just that I'm smarter than a turkey," replied Johnny as he walked away.

The Marvelous Lamps

IN MAY, 1848, an exciting story appeared in the weekly newspaper. It told that gold had been discovered in the Sacramento Valley of California. Johnny heard the news first from the banker in Moravia. "Many men will rush out there hoping to get rich quickly," the banker said. "Doubtless some men from right here in Moravia will join the fortune hunters."

Johnny had come to the bank to deposit money from his bear bank. He thought of how slowly he saved money and wished he knew of a way to get rich quickly. He could readily understand why men would rush to California to seek their fortunes. If he only were a few years older, he might go to California, too.

"Yes, sir," added the banker, "some of the men who are on their way to California hope to get rich quickly just as Aladdin did by getting help from a genie."

"I don't understand," said Johnny. "Who was Aladdin and what's a genie?"

"Aladdin is a character in a book called *The Thousand and One Nights,* which I have at home. The next time you come to the bank, I'll loan it to you."

"Oh thank you," said Johnny, "but please tell me a little about Aladdin now."

"Well, he was the obstinate, disobedient son of a poor widow," replied the banker. "Even though he was this undeserving kind of boy, he found a magic lamp. Whenever he rubbed the lamp, a genie or magic creature appeared and offered to give him anything he asked."

Johnny stood thinking a few minutes. "Do you mean that he didn't deserve what he asked the genie to get for him?"

The banker was pleased to know that Johnny understood. "Yes, and that will be true of many men on their way to California to find gold," he said. "They never have amounted to anything and won't deserve to get rich just by picking up nuggets of gold. Most people who want something for nothing aren't very deserving."

A week or so later Eliza's father, John Davison, visited the Rockefeller home. He told about one of his neighbors who had helped to form a company to travel to California. They had put up $500.00 apiece and planned to travel by ship all the way around South America to California. Each man had taken along only a sea chest, a gun, a pick, and shovel.

"Weren't they afraid to take a chance on going so far?" asked Johnny.

"Oh, no," replied his grandfather. "When they left, they were singing that foolish song, 'Oh, Susannah,' which is so popular now."

"I guess I haven't heard that song," said Eliza. "How does it go?"

"I know," said the schoolteacher, Sophie Parker, who still lived at the Rockefeller home. Then she sang the following lines:

"It rained all day the night I left.
The weather was so dry;
The sun so hot I froze to death.
Oh, Susannah, don't you cry."

The tune was so catchy that Johnny and the other children clapped their hands as Sophie sang. "Sing some more," they cried.

"Let me sing you these two lines which are especially interesting," said Sophie.

"Oh, Susannah, don't you cry for me.
I'm off from Alabama with my banjo on
my knee."

Then Sophie added, "The gold-seekers have modified the second line and sing it like this:

> "I'm off to California with my washbowl on my knee."

"Why do they use the word washbowl instead of the word banjo?" asked Johnny.

"Because they are looking forward to using a washbowl to wash out gold nuggets if they find any," replied Sophie.

At this point John Davison interrupted. "One thing is sure," he said. "They won't find any gold nuggets unless they are willing to do hard, back-breaking work, and even then they may not find any." He turned to speak directly to Eliza. "I'm surprised that your adventurous husband hasn't fallen for this kind of gamble."

A few days later Big Bill happened to return home. He felt very disappointed when he heard about the company which the men had formed to go to California. "If I had been here, I certainly would have joined," he said.

"We're glad you didn't go," said Eliza. "We miss you when you go away."

Big Bill smiled and sat down beside Eliza for a few minutes to visit. "There's no use fussing about water that's gone under the bridge," he said, "so let's talk about something else. What's new here in Moravia."

"Well, I've heard that the hotel has installed some marvelous new lamps," replied Eliza. "These lamps are supposed to give off light by burning something called kerosene. Do you know what kerosene is?"

"Yes," replied Big Bill. "It's a new kind of fuel to burn in lamps."

That evening Big Bill happily visited with the members of his family. He hadn't seen the twins, Frank and Francis, since they were babies. Frank, who was large for his age, was most active of all the six Rockefeller children. Francis, on the other hand, was still weak and puny. "I'm afraid that he isn't long for this world," said Eliza, wiping away a tear.

Big Bill patted her shoulder and said, "I hope you are wrong, but if you're not, remember that comforting verse in the Bible, 'The Lord God will wipe away tears from all faces.' "

As Eliza listened to these words, her face brightened. "Yes, I remember," she replied. "Thank you, Bill, for reminding me."

The next day Big Bill took Johnny into Moravia. He was eager to see the new kerosene lamps at the hotel which his wife had mentioned. Johnny wanted to go to the bank to get the book which the banker had promised to lend him.

Big Bill went directly to the hotel and Johnny went to the bank. When Johnny returned to the hotel with his book, he found his father visiting with several men on the front porch, so he sat down in a chair and started to read his book. He soon stopped, however, after reading this meaningless introduction:

> "It is related, o auspicious king, that there was once—but Allah knows all—in the antiquities of time and the passage of the age and of the moment . . ."

After Johnny stopped reading, he listened to the conversation which the men were carrying on nearby. "Mark my word," said one of them, "this new kerosene, which is distilled from coal, will revolutionize lighting in the world. It's much better than whale oil."

"Yes, I agree," said Big Bill, picking up the conversation. "Kerosene is here to stay. The process of making kerosene is called refining. Someday not too far off somebody will make a fortune in this business of refining."

As Johnny sat holding his book, he thought,

"Why read about a make-believe lamp when a truly marvelous lamp is right here before me? I must learn more about this new business of refining in which someone will make a fortune."

During the next few weeks, Big Bill and Johnny made several other trips into Moravia. In the meantime little Francis became gradually weaker and died. Big Bill tried hard to comfort his grieving wife and children. "You're a tower of strength to us," said Eliza tearfully. "We're thankful you were at home."

Big Bill was also a tower of strength in another way that summer. He joined a crusade which was conducted by a national organization to fight the use of alcholic drinks. He took this crusade seriously and traveled widely through the countryside, speaking against "Demon Rum." Johnny often rode along with him to see the crowds and to listen to his lectures.

On these trips through the countryside Johnny was very proud of Big Bill. He thought that he was one of the most brilliant persons in the world. "I'm surely fortunate to have such an outstanding father," he said to himself.

Along the Susquehanna

Gradually the people of Moravia discovered what Big Bill did for a living. They found out that he sold patent medicines when he went away on his trips. These medicines were supposed to cure many sorts of ailments, such as cancer, tuberculosis, arthritis, and rheumatism.

In those days there were few doctors and drug stores. Many persons traveled about the country selling patent medicines to people. Some even put on free shows, called medicine shows, to attract crowds to whom they could sell their medicines. Some of these sales persons were good dependable citizens, but others were frauds.

Some even pretended to be doctors, although they had no training whatever in medicine.

When the people in Moravia found out that Big Bill sold patent medicines, some of them turned against him. In addition some of the people to whom he had sold medicines brought suit against him, claiming that his medicine had failed to cure them. These accusations made him exceedingly angry because he felt that he was actually helping people and that nobody had a right to challenge what he was doing.

Later that summer when he left on his next trip, he vowed that he never would return to Moravia. He assured Eliza, however, that while he was gone, he would look for a new place to live and send for her and the children to join him. Eliza trusted him and felt sure that eventually he would keep his word.

After Big Bill left, the family had very trying times. Since the people of Moravia no longer trusted him as they had before, Eliza had a difficult time getting food and clothing for the family. She even had to sell some of the family possessions.

During this troublesome period, Johnny decided to sell his flock of turkeys. Proudly he returned home and offered the money to his mother, but much to his surprise she refused to accept it. "Add it to your savings in the bank," she said. "Someday you may need those savings to help you get started in life."

In the ensuing months Eliza turned to religion for comfort from her many problems. There was no church nearby where she could attend services, so she frequently read the Bible at home. Now and then she read selections to her children to inspire them with hope for the future. "The Lord will provide for tomorrow and its needs," she told them reassuringly.

In the spring of 1850, after many months of

waiting, Eliza received a letter from Big Bill. He reported that he had rented a house near Owego, New York, and would wait for her and the children to join him there. This town was the county seat of Tioga County, not far from Richford where Johnny had been born.

At once Eliza and the children made preparations to move. She realized that the trip would be very difficult because much of the road was merely a trail leading through the woods. For this reason she decided to take only the few belongings which she could load into a small one-horse wagon.

When everything was ready, she climbed up to the front seat to drive the horse. Lucy and Mary Ann sat beside her with Lucy holding little Frank. Johnny and William sat on bundles in the rear, dangling their feet over the back.

The trip proved to be even more difficult than Eliza had anticipated. Near evening she decided to stop at a wayside inn so the children could get a good night's rest. Soon, however, she regretted stopping because the inn was crowded with noisy guests.

Even the dining room at the inn was filled with din and confusion. Eliza urged the children to eat rapidly so they could return to their room as soon as possible. Most of all she wanted them to get some sleep. Fortunately the bedroom was quiet and comfortable.

Eliza, Lucy, Mary Ann, and little Frank slept in the bed and Johnny and William slept on the floor. All the others went to sleep immediately, but Johnny lay away for a while, wondering what his new home would be like and what he could do there.

Late the next afternoon Eliza and the children arrived at their new home, glad to end their long journey. Big Bill was there to meet them and gave them a hearty welcome. Quickly they unloaded their possessions and sat down for a long happy evening together.

The new house was located about three miles from Owego, fairly close to the Susquehanna River. Big Bill stayed at home for a few weeks to help the family get settled. Each day he took Johnny and William on trips through the neighborhood. On one of their first trips, he took them for a walk along the Susquehanna River. For a few minutes the boys stood silently and watched boats and rafts travel slowly up and down the river. Finally Johnny exclaimed, "How beautiful this Susquehanna River is! Where does it flow from here?"

"It flows far to the southeast and empties into Chesapeake Bay, which is along the Atlantic Ocean," replied Big Bill.

"I've studied about the Atlantic Ocean in school," said Johnny. "It's a big ocean between the United States and Europe. Many people from countries in Europe have come to the United States to live."

On succeeding days Johnny and William made many trips to the river. One day they wrote their names on a piece of paper and placed it in a bottle. They put a cork in the bottle and tossed it into the river. "Who knows?" said Johnny. "Some boy in England, France, or Germany may find this bottle and wonder who John D. or William Rockefeller is."

That summer the family had several happy carefree weeks together. At last Big Bill announced that he would have to take off again to sell more patent medicine. Eliza understood, but both she and the children were very sad about his leaving. Life seemed far less exciting for them when he was away.

Soon after Big Bill left, a neighbor family offered to take Eliza and the children to church services in Owego. From then on they attended church services regularly each Sunday. All the children seemed to enjoy the services except Frank, who sighed loudly, twisted and turned, and slumped way down in his seat, waiting for the services to end.

Johnny usually sat beside Frank during church services. Finally one Sunday he became so annoyed with Frank's behavior that he lost his temper and boxed Frank's ears. Frank turned on him in a furious rage and cried, "You'll be mighty sorry you hit me. I'll get even with you some way. Just wait and see."

By now Johnny was so sorry about what he had done that he scarcely heard Frank's threat. He bowed his head in prayer and promised never to do such a thing again.

The first year the family lived near Owego, Eliza arranged for Lucy, Johnny, and William to attend a school which was conducted in a neighbor's house. The following year she decided to send them to a private school, called Owego Academy. She had to pay tuition for them to attend this school, but she wanted them to associate with the sons and daughters of the best families in the community. "Every man is known by the company he keeps," she said.

Johnny enrolled at Owego Academy as John Davison Rockefeller, and both teachers and students called him John. He was exceedingly pleased to have everyone call him John rather than Johnny because it made him feel as if he were growing up. Actually he was, for on his next birthday he would be thirteen years old.

In his work at the Academy John proved to be a whiz in arithmetic. He delighted in playing a mathematical game called numerica which required doing problems mentally. Nearly always he won whenever he played this game.

Another of his favorite games was chess, which also required brainwork. He never made a move without taking time to consider it from all angles. Once an opponent became annoyed because he took so much time and cried out, "Hurry up, John. Why do you take so long?"

"Because I want to be sure of what may happen before I move," he replied.

"What's the difference?" retorted his friend. "We're only playing a game."

Johnny looked at him reprovingly. "Yes, I know, but the object is to win."

During his first summer vacation from the Academy, John had a couple of financial experiences which greatly influenced his life in the future. First, he had an opportunity to lend $50.00 to a neighbor at seven percent interest. His mother encouraged him to make the loan because she trusted the neighbor. "I'm sure you won't regret it," she said.

Later on he had an opportunity to dig potatoes for another neighbor, which turned out to

be a hot, back-breaking job. When he finished the job, the neighbor paid him three shillings, which amounted to $1.23½.

He was fully satisfied with this pay until the first neighbor returned his $50.00, plus $3.50 interest. As he counted this interest money, he could scarcely believe his eyes. "Why are you surprised?" asked his mother.

"Because I have just learned something important," he said, "that capital has greater earning power than muscle."

Later on he enlarged upon this theme by saying, "I have learned to let money be my servant rather than to let myself be a slave to money. I'll always try to remember this lesson."

John managed to keep busy through the entire vacation, but he was very happy when it became time to return to the Academy in the fall. He felt that going to school was an important way to prepare for life.

Lucy, John, and William regularly walked to the Academy to school. Their route led them along Front Street, past the elegant homes of some of the most prosperous families in the community. Often as they walked by, some of their schoolmates came out to join them.

One morning the son of one of the wealthiest citizens came out to join John on his way to school. The two boys talked about what they hoped to accomplish in life. "Some day I hope to own all the land for miles and miles around Owego," said the son of the wealthy citizen. "What do you want most when you grow up?"

At once John thought of the money which he had been saving. "I want money," he said, "maybe as much as a hundred thousand dollars." Little did he know that he would accumulate many times this amount in his lifetime.

From time to time John told his mother about walking to school with these schoolmates. He knew that she wanted her children to associate with the children from the elegant homes. Somehow it helped to repay her for the sacrifices she was making in order to send her children to the Academy.

John fully understood how difficult it was for Eliza to pay their tuition at the Academy. He felt obliged to repay her by taking his school work seriously. Lucy and William, on the other hand, felt no such obligation. They failed to study and frittered away the hours, as if going to school wasn't important.

As time passed, John became greatly disturbed about Lucy and William. He kept quiet, however, until he heard a teacher scold William for failing to study. Then, on the way home, he said, "I'm surprised at you, William. You know how hard it is for Mother to send us to the Academy. How can you treat her like this?"

William was still hurt by the scolding which

the teacher had given him. Now John's scolding was more than he could take. "Mother really doesn't care how much I learn from poring through books at school," he retorted. "She is more interested in my associating with children of the right people here. If you don't believe me, just ask her."

At first John was shocked by this challenge, but after thinking the matter over briefly, he decided that William was partially right. After all, his mother hadn't talked about sending her children to the Academy to learn, but rather to associate with the sons and daughters from the prosperous families in the community. "You may have a point," he admitted.

"Well, hallelujah!" exclaimed William.

"But that doesn't mean that I completely agree with you," John continued doggedly.

"Why not?" asked William.

"Because I think you should study more for

your own good, and possibly I should study somewhat less for my own good," said John.

From then on, John tried to take his work less seriously, but somehow he just couldn't change his ways. He always had to plan carefully everything he did. This trait bothered some of his classmates, who wondered why he didn't immediately pitch in and do things.

One day John overheard a schoolmate criticizing him in a conversation with William. "Your brother always has to figure out the best way to do something before he moves a muscle," said the schoolmate. "Why does he take so much time before he starts?"

"Because he's methodical and wants to plan exactly what to do before he moves a muscle," replied William. "You'll have to admit that he does everything well."

"Yes," replied the classmate reluctantly.

"John believes thoroughly in planning," continued William. "He doesn't believe that success or failure comes about by accident. Whatever it is, it's simple justice."

The schoolmate thought for a moment, temporarily puzzled by this remark. "Then he must be awfully hard to live with," he added.

"Oh, no, not at all," replied William. "He is always fair and willing to listen to other persons' opinions. The only time he ever argues is after he has reached a decision. You can't expect more of a fellow than that."

John was very much pleased with William's comments during this conversation. He was glad to find out that William still approved of him even though he recently had scolded him for not studying. Maybe William was more serious-minded than he had thought.

At this same time John was having trouble with Frank, who never had forgiven him for boxing his ears in church. There didn't seem to be anything John could do or say to change Frank's attitude. "He must needs go where the devil drives," John muttered to himself. This was a quotation from a sermon that he recently had heard in church, but he never had thought of it before in connection with Frank. Now that he had done so, he wondered whether he had been quite fair to Frank.

Sometimes he feared that his mother was too strict with Frank. In recent weeks she seemed to lean heavily on a verse in the Book of Proverbs in the Bible. This verse stated that a person who spurned the rod hated his son, but that a person who diligently punished his son, truly loved him.

Eliza always had been a strict disciplinarian, but usually had been willing to accept reasonable excuses for wrongdoing. Now she seemed to feel that any wrongdoing was inexcusable, as John and William were soon to find out.

All winter they had gone skating after school on the Susquehanna River. They welcomed the opportunity to skate after being cooped up in a stuffy schoolroom for hours. In March, however, after the weather began to warm up, Eliza warned them not to skate on the ice any more. "The thawing season has come and the ice may not support you," she said.

"Have you tried the ice, Mama?" asked John.

"No," she replied. "I don't have to taste a rotten apple to find out that it's bad."

That night after John was sure his mother had gone to bed, he suggested to William that they steal out of the house to test the ice. "How can we test it?" asked William.

"We'll place a couple of bags of sand on a board and slide the board out on the ice. Then if the ice doesn't crack or give way under the weight of the sand, we'll know that it's still safe for us to use for skating."

"Well, I surely hope that it's still safe," said William.

"So do I," said John, leading the way, "but we'll soon find out."

The boys carried the weighted board down to the edge of the ice. Moments later, just as they were ready to give it a shove, they heard a boy shouting frantically, "Help! Help!"

For perhaps the first time in his life, John didn't stop to plan. He raced out onto the ice, with William following close behind him. "Keep yelling," he called to the struggling boy, "so we can tell where you are."

"Be careful or you'll break through the ice, too," wailed the boy.

John slowed down at this warning, and William bumped into him. They both fell, but fortunately the ice didn't give way. "We'd better crawl from here on," said John. Then he called to the boy in the water, "Where are you?"

"Right here," replied the boy.

John looked and in the scant moonlight he could see the boy waving his arms only a few feet away. "Hold onto my legs," he said to William, "and pull as I pull."

Together they managed to pull the frantic boy out of the hole in the ice. Then cautiously they led him to the bank. "Thank you for saving my life," he said feelingly. "I would have drowned if you hadn't happened to rescue me."

John and William walked homeward slowly and slipped into the house again. They were so shocked by what had happened that they could scarcely get to sleep. "We'll have to tell Mama in the morning," said John.

"Yes, I suppose so," said William. "But she surely will forgive us."

"I hope so," said John.

The next morning the boys promptly confessed to Eliza about slipping out and going to the river to test the ice. She was so angry that she scarcely waited for them to tell about saving the boy's life. "Surely you don't expect me to praise you for being heroic," she cried. "Fortunately all of you are safe, but you could just as readily be in the river."

John tried to explain further, but his mother wouldn't listen. Instead she ordered William to bring in a horsewhip from the stable. She hadn't whipped either of them for years, and they had never expected her to whip them again. After all, they were big boys, much too big to be whipped, especially by their mother. When William came in with the whip, she said, "Now turn around and lean over the backs of these chairs. And don't expect me to be the least bit easy on you."

"Aren't you going to make them take their breeches down?" Frank called out accusingly. "You always make me take mine down."

"No, they are too old for that," said Eliza. "In fact, they are too old to be whipped."

Moments later she swished the whip and gave each boy a sound thrashing. They took their punishment without complaint, because they knew they were guilty. What bothered John most was not the humiliation of being punished or the pain from the lashes of the whip. Instead it was the devilish laughter of Frank, who whooped it up with every lash of the whip.

No Pictures at School

ONE DAY Dr. Smythe, the headmaster of the Owego Academy, announced that a photographer would soon come to take a picture of the students. "I don't know exactly when he will come, so I suggest that you wear your best bib and tucker for a few days," he said.

This announcement created no problem for most boys and girls in the school. The boys, like their fathers, wore rich woolen tailor-made suits. They wore shirts made from the finest bleached linen and broad flowing ties made from the most expensive silk.

The Rockefeller boys had no such elegant

clothes to wear. Their mother made most of their clothes and allowed them to wear their best clothes only on Sunday. "Dr. Smythe must be crazy to ask you students to dress up for school every day," she said. "Well, you boys certainly aren't going to."

Lucy no longer attended the Academy, but she fully understood how well the boys and girls there were dressed. At once she spoke in behalf of John and William. "Oh, Mama," she pleaded, "let them wear their best clothes for a few days. What harm will it do?"

Eliza looked sternly at Lucy. "What harm will it do?" she cried. "Surely you know that boys just can't wear clothes every day and keep them neat and clean."

"Well, most boys at school wear good clothes every day," said Lucy stubbornly.

"That may be," replied Eliza, "but I won't allow my boys to be that foolish."

Several days later when the photographer came to the school, John and William still were wearing their everyday clothes. Mr. Smythe instructed all the students except John and William to form a group to have their pictures taken. "I'm sorry to leave you two boys out," he said in an apologetic tone of voice.

By now John had come to expect that he and William would be left out. "Oh, that's all right, Mr. Smythe," he said. "Don't worry about it, because we understand."

William really had hoped to have his picture taken. As John led him to the back of the room, he whispered angrily, "Don't speak for me. I didn't want to be left out."

"Well, being left out is better than having our everyday clothes stand out like sore thumbs in the picture," said John.

"Well Mama's to blame for not letting us wear our best clothes," complained William.

"No," argued John in return, "Mr. Smythe is to blame. He should have arranged for the photographer to come at a certain time on a certain day. If he had, Mama would have allowed us to wear our best clothes to school. Then we would be up there now having our pictures taken along with the others."

From the back of the room, John and William watched the students getting ready to have their pictures taken. The girls were busy fussing with their hair or fluffing the ruffles of their dresses. The boys were busy straightening their ties or buttoning their coats. "Now get set, boys and girls," called the photographer. "Take on pleasant expressions and hold them until I tell you to relax."

John almost laughed out loud as he watched schoolmates posing for the pictures. Some tried to smile but couldn't, some grinned so widely that they showed all their teeth, and others merely stared off blankly into space. They stood posing in this manner until the photographer told them they could relax.

That evening on the way home, William still was grieving because he had been left out of the picture. "What's the difference?" said John, trying to ease his feelings. "In a few years you won't remember these schoolmates anyway."

"Oh, yes, I will," William argued. "I'll always remember them."

John shrugged. "If you had any money, I'd bet you on it," he said.

"Then you must be sure you're right," said William. "Otherwise you wouldn't be willing to bet. But I'm more like Papa. I'm willing to take a chance on being wrong."

"Yes, you're right about Papa," said John. "He surely likes to take chances."

Strangely, that same evening Big Bill came home in his Conestoga wagon. He was in high spirits and obviously had made money while he had been gone. He happily presented each child with a five-dollar gold piece.

All the children were very pleased with their

gold pieces. Nine-year-old Mary exclaimed, "Oh how pretty my coin is! I'd like to wear it on a chain around my neck."

"Oh, no!" said Big Bill. "It's not intended for that. I'll get you something special to wear around your neck."

"Bill!" said his wife. "Please don't talk to her like that. You'll spoil her by making such rash promises."

Later that evening Big Bill made an important announcement to both his wife and children. "When I leave next time, you're all going with me," he said. "We're going to move a long distance away to a section of northeastern Ohio, called the Western Reserve."

This news came as such a surprise to Eliza that she turned white and gripped the arms of her chair. "Bill," she said after a moment, "are you sure that this is a wise move? We're already living in a fine community and have many good friends here. Besides, John and William are attending the Owego Academy here."

"Don't worry about their education in the Western Reserve, Eliza," replied Big Bill. "I'm sure that Cleveland with 20,000 inhabitants will have good schools."

"Will we live in Cleveland?" exclaimed Lucy, greatly excited.

"No, not at first," replied Big Bill. "We'll live in Strongsville, about a dozen miles south. I am sure you will like it there."

"Tell us more about Cleveland," said John.

"Well, Cleveland is located on Lake Erie at the edge of a fine farming area," Big Bill explained. "Already it's an important trading center with both railroad and lake-boat transportation. Someday I predict it will become one of the leading business centers in the country."

John listened closely to his father's conversation. He felt that Cleveland must be a good place for a growing boy to live. He only wished that his father was planning to settle there in stead of in the small town of Strongsville twelve miles away.

"How soon will we have to move, Papa?" asked Lucy, eager for more information.

"We'll leave that to your mother," said Big Bill, looking inquiringly at Eliza.

"Not until John and William finish their year at the Academy," said Eliza.

"Yes, we'll certainly wait until they finish school," said Big Bill. "The late spring will be a fine time for us to go. Then everything along the way will be beautiful."

Big Bill now talked about how long the trip would be. "We'll travel hundreds of miles and have to spend many days and nights on the road. That's why I brought the Conestoga wagon."

"Will we pass through Richford along the way?" asked Eliza. "If so, you may wish to say good-by to your parents. Since we're moving so far away, you may never see them again."

"That's a good idea," said Big Bill. "First we'll go to Richford to see my parents. Then we'll head straight west to Lake Erie. You children will be surprised when you see this lake. It's so big that it looks more like an ocean than a lake."

John's heart leaped. He had never seen a lake any larger than Lake Owasco. He could scarcely believe that one would be so big that it would look like an ocean. "I'll just have to wait to see," he said doubtfully.

The Long Trek to Ohio

John was eager to see the village of Richford again. He could scarcely remember anything about it, since he had moved from there when he was only four years old. The most he recalled was that he had lived in a house with apple trees round about and a dark cellar beneath.

He watched closely as the wagon rolled past neat little shops and stores in the center of the town. He looked inquiringly at people walking along the wooden sidewalks. "Do you know any of these people, Mama?" he asked.

"No," replied Eliza. "Remember that we haven't lived here for a long time."

Big Bill drove straight through the village without stopping. Soon Johnny spotted a small house on the crest of a hill that looked vaguely familiar. He looked again and noticed that the house was surrounded by apple trees. Yes, this must be the house where he was born.

Moments later Big Bill brought the wagon to a halt. "Well, here's the house where we formerly lived," he said. "Take a good look, because you may never see it again."

"I remember the apple trees," said Johnny. "You remember them, too, don't you Mama? You picked apples from them to make pies."

"Yes, and I remember how quickly my apple pies disappeared," laughed Eliza.

Big Bill kept on driving until he reached the home of his parents, Godfrey and Lucy Rockefeller. His father was away from home, and his mother was busy supervising two workmen who were building a stone fence near the house. She picked out the big stones and told the workmen exactly where to put them.

John stayed outside with his grandmother to watch the workmen. He was intrigued with the way in which she directed them. "When you're in the driver's seat, you must handle the reins," she said. "That will be good for you to remember when you grow up."

John nodded. "I'll remember," he said.

As usual, Big Bill was restless and wanted to get started again. After an hour or so, he asked Eliza and the children to take their places in the wagon and started to drive westward. From this time on John could hardly wait to see Lake Erie, which his father had described as big like an ocean. Days later he was thrilled to look out on this great body of water.

The trip along the lake was slow and treacherous. Much of the land was low and swampy, covered with soft, silty clay. Frequently the

wagon wheels bogged down in the soft clay and the wheels became stuck. Then Big Bill and the boys had to dig them loose.

In some places there were corduroy roads. These consisted of logs placed close together crossways of the road to keep vehicles from miring in the soft soil. As Big Bill drove over these corduroy roads, the wagon jolted from log to log, and everybody and everything in the wagon jolted, too. Usually John and William jumped out and walked to avoid the jolting.

After days of rough, slow traveling, the family came to Erie, Pennsylvania. This city, which was located on Lake Erie, had a fine natural harbor. John marveled as he looked at the many boats, some big and some little. Big Bill explained that most of the larger boats were used for hauling lumber and grain to market in other cities on the lake. Many of the smaller boats were used for fishing.

Erie was an attractive city with well-kept houses and lawns. Scattered here and there were apple, peach and cherry orchards and gardens filled with all sorts of growing vegetables.

"This surely is a beautiful city," said Lucy as she looked about. "I hope that Cleveland will be just as beautiful."

"Well, it really is," said Big Bill, "but Cleveland has a different history from Erie. The early settlers built Cleveland along a little river, called the Cuyahoga River, which flows into the lake. This river was their only harbor because there was no natural harbor along the lake. For this reason most people thought that Cleveland never would have an opportunity to grow. They thought that it always would remain a paltry village, because it lacked a good harbor."

"With 20,000 inhabitants, it certainly is no longer a paltry village," said John. "What happened? How has it managed to grow?"

"It has grown chiefly because of the determination of its citizens," replied Big Bill. "It was settled by people who were willing to scratch and dig for a living. They began to ship lumber from nearby forests and grain from nearby farms, using the Cuyahoga River as a harbor. They even shipped hides and pelts from wild animals which they caught.

"As time passed," he continued, "they found that the harbor along the small Cuyahoga River was too small for their purposes. Finally they decided to build a harbor by constructing a barrier, or wall, out in the lake to hold back the rough waters which frequently pounded the shore. This barrier formed a sort of bay with quiet water which boats could use safely."

"I guess the people now are glad that they built this harbor," said John.

"Yes, with this fine harbor, Cleveland is sure to grow rapidly from now on," said Big Bill.

When the Rockefellers reached Cleveland, Big Bill suggested that they drive directly to Strongsville to get settled in their new home. John and the other children were surprised and pleased to find that this new house was much larger than any they had ever lived in before. Since Eliza now would have more work to do, Big Bill immediately promised to hire a girl to help her. This hired girl would stay full time at the house and really become a part of the family.

Building for the Future

SOON AFTER the Rockefeller family was comfortably settled in Strongsville, Big Bill made a business trip into Cleveland. When he returned, he made an important announcement to John. "I've arranged for you to enter Central High School in the city," he said.

At first John was too surprised and stunned to speak. Finally he asked, "How can I go to school so far away?"

"You'll have to stay in Cleveland," replied his father. "I've secured a place for you to room and board not far from the school."

"Will this really be good for John?" asked

Eliza doubtfully. "Should he go to an ordinary high school after attending Owego Academy?"

"Let me explain," said Big Bill. "Central High School isn't an ordinary high school. Instead it's the aristocratic high school where children from all the well-to-do families go. I've kept in mind that we want John to associate with children from good families."

"Oh," replied Eliza. "Then you seem to have made a good decision."

In the fall of 1854, at the age of fourteen, John stepped into his classroom at Central High School. He inquired for the teacher, but she hadn't arrived yet, so he waited at the door for her to come. Inside the room the students who had attended the school before were talking and laughing happily.

Before long one of the students in the room happened to notice John and came over to talk with him. "Hello," he said in a friendly tone of voice. "I don't seem to know you. I'm Mark A. Hanna. What's your name?"

"My name is John Davison Rockefeller," replied John rather warily.

"Are you new in town or just in Central High School?" asked Mark.

"I'm new both in town and in Central High School," replied John. "My family lives in Strongsville, Ohio."

Mark raised his eyebrows. "That's interesting," he said. "How can you attend school here when your family lives in Strongsville?"

"My father has arranged for me to room and board near here," explained John.

"Well, since you're new, you are probably anxious to get acquainted," said Mark. "Come with me to meet some of my friends."

Mark led John into the room and started to introduce him. Repeatedly he told the others that John was living alone in Cleveland. Evidently he thought that this information would lead them to think that John was very important.

Soon some of the boys invited him to play soccer with them after school. This was a new kind of game which required kicking a football. John wasn't very much interested in playing and kicked the ball carelessly. "Keep your eyes on the ball when you kick it," Mark cautioned him.

"Yes, I know," replied John.

A few minutes later on his very next turn, he kicked the ball carelessly again. His toe hit it on one side and caused it to go far off the mark. It sailed over a low fence at one side of the field and hit a man who was standing on a ladder to paint a house.

The man climbed down the ladder and picked up the ball. He leaped over the fence in a furious rage and strode up to the group of boys. Angrily he brandished the ball and asked, "Which of you boys kicked this ball?"

"I did," replied John, "but I didn't mean to hit you. I'm sorry and apologize."

"Bosh!" yelled the man. He threw down the ball and started to threaten John with his fists. At once John thought of the Old Testament adage, "An eye for an eye, a tooth for a tooth." He stood bravely, willing to take a beating, if necessary. After all, he had hit the man, even though only by accident.

Quickly Mark, who was big and strong, came to John's rescue. He stepped between John and the man and started to exchange blows with him. Soon the man gave up fighting and walked sullenly back to the house.

Afterwards, John thanked Mark for helping him. He explained that he hadn't fought because he believed in the old Testament adage, and felt that he was guilty. Then Mark looked at him in surprise and asked, "Do you really believe in that Old Testament stuff?"

"Yes, I do," replied John.

While John had lived at Owego, he had formed the habit of attending church services on Sunday. After he moved to Cleveland, he looked about for a nearby church to attend. Soon he located the Erie Street Baptist Church, where the pastor was J. Hyatt Smith.

John liked Pastor Smith and attended Sunday school regularly. He became acquainted with many church members and went to many church parties and picnics. Before long he looked upon the church as a home away from home.

Only adults could be baptized to become members of the church, but John was eager to become a member as early as possible. In 1854, when he was fifteen years old, he applied for membership and was accepted. Under the regulations of the church, he had a choice of being baptized in several ways, but he chose total immersion, or being placed under water.

After the baptismal service, Pastor Smith asked him how he felt. "I didn't expect to feel any different from before, but I do," replied John. "I feel much like Saint Paul, who wrote in his letter to the Corinthians, 'When I was a child, I spoke like a child. Now that I am a man I have put away childish things.' "

"That's not exactly what he wrote," said Pastor Smith, laughing, "but it's close."

During John's second year at Central High School, he became better and better acquainted. He attended many school events and school parties. Mostly he associated with boys, but one day he met a girl who especially attracted his attention. Her name was Laura Celestia Spelman, but everybody called her Cettie.

Both John and Cettie took piano lessons at school. His only opportunity to see her was while they were in class, because a coachman regularly came with a handsome carriage to take her home. Her father was a prominent political leader in Cleveland and the state of Ohio.

During John's final months at Central High School he became interested in attending college. On one of his trips home, he said to his mother, "Many of my friends are planning to go to college. I hope I can go, too."

Eliza encouraged him with his college ambitions. She pointed out that there were several good colleges which he might attend. She was proud of him for wanting to get more education.

John talked with his friend Mark about going to college. Mark explained that he planned to attend nearby Western Reserve University for a year. Then he would go into the wholesale grocery business with his father. "My father only has an elementary education," he said. "Now he wants me to go to college to see whether I can learn any newfangled ways of doing things. That's why I'm going to college for a year."

Finally John discussed going to college with his father. "Why bother?" asked Big Bill. "In this world people get along by using their wits, not by cramming their heads."

John explained what Mark's father had said about learning newfangled ways in college. "Yes, but Mark knows exactly what he is going to do," said Big Bill. "He is going into business with his father, whereas you have no idea of what you are going to do."

"Well, I'm sure that I want to go into some kind of business," said John.

Big Bill smiled. "Then all you need is practical training for business, maybe a course in bookkeeping," he said. "You seem to have a liking for figures."

"Yes, I do," said John.

Back at school John asked his mathematics teacher whether he knew of a school that taught bookkeeping. His teacher recommended Folsom's Commercial College in Cleveland. Immediately after John graduated from Central High School in May, 1955, he enrolled at this college where he studied hard through the summer.

Commission Merchant

John attended Folsom's Commercial College for three months, studying bookkeeping and several subjects dealing with business and banking. In August, 1855, when he completed his work, he was awarded a certificate of excellence. Now, with this certificate and his high school diploma, he started to look for work.

In seeking employment, he hoped to obtain more than just an ordinary job. He wanted to work where he could learn a business and either come to manage it or establish a similar business of his own. He decided not to take a job that wouldn't offer these possibilities.

First he made a list of the business places or companies that he felt would offer the best opportunities. Then he walked from one section of the city to another to seek employment, but was rejected repeatedly. Some business places turned him down rudely, some politely, and some suggested that he come back later. Following each visit he made notes to help him remember what the business was like.

After his first futile efforts in looking for employment, he decided to revisit the office of Hewitt and Tuttle. He had noted that these men were produce commission merchants who bought large quantities of fruits, vegetables, and other food products to sell to local Cleveland stores. On his second trip to the office he talked with the senior partner, Isaac Hewitt. "How old are you?" asked Mr. Hewitt.

John liked this white-haired, pink-cheeked businessman and felt that he would make a good

employer. "I just turned sixteen, sir, but I have a diploma from Central High School and a certificate of excellence from Folsom Commercial College," replied John. "I am especially interested in a job as bookkeeper."

"Just why do you want to work for our company?" asked Mr. Hewitt.

"Because you have a broad type of business, with opportunities to become acquainted with many kinds of activities," replied John. Then, seeing that Mr. Hewitt was smiling encouragingly, he added, "I feel that by working for you I can get a liberal education about things that I can't possibly learn out of books."

Mr. Hewitt leaned back in his chair and rubbed his chin thoughtfully. "Well, Mr. Tuttle acts as our bookkeeper," he said, "but I'm sure he wouldn't mind giving up this responsibility." He hesitated a moment, then added, "We'll give you a try. Report back here this afternoon."

"Thank you, sir, for giving me a chance," said John, rising. "I'll be here."

John left the office feeling as if he were walking on air. He wanted an opportunity to think, so he strolled out on a pier overlooking Lake Erie. There he stood briefly, enjoying the serene expanse of water.

In a few minutes he pulled a sandwich from his pocket. Before he started to eat, he paused as usual to utter a little prayer. "I am blessed, Lord," he said, "and shall be thankful all the days of my life."

As he ate, he continued to think. He recalled that Mr. Hewitt hadn't mentioned salary, but he felt sure that there was no cause to worry. He needed money, but more than anything else at present he needed a job.

After he finished eating his sandwich, he returned to the Hewitt and Tuttle office to take his new job. He arrived before the two owners had returned from lunch, so he sat down on a bench to wait. While he was waiting, he had an opportunity to watch some of the employees carry on their work.

He noted that all of them seemed to know exactly what to do and to be doing it well and cheerfully. Their behavior indicated that the owners of the company were exacting but fair. How fortunate he was to be offered a trial here!

In a few minutes Mr. Hewitt and Mr. Tuttle returned from lunch. "Well, young Rockefeller," said Mr. Hewitt, "we've decided to give you a three-month trial as our bookkeeper. At the end of that time, we'll evaluate your services and determine whether or not they seem to justify our retaining you. Are you willing to start work on the basis of these terms?"

"Yes," replied John, "and I promise to do a trustworthy job for you."

"Good," said Hewitt. "Mr. Tuttle will show

you where you are to work and will explain our system of bookkeeping to you."

Mr. Tuttle led the way to a desk, where John would have to do most of his work. He explained the ledgers and other record books and pointed out pens, pencils, and blotters which he could use. "Is there anything you don't understand?" he asked. "If so, tell me before you do something wrong."

John detected a note of worry in Mr. Tuttle's voice. "You seem to have made everything clear, and I believe I understand what I'm supposed to do," replied John. "If I find out otherwise, I promise to tell you."

Mr. Tuttle nodded. "That's fine," he said, "and I wish you well."

At once John began to turn the pages of the ledgers. He knew that by reading these pages carefully and consecutively, he could get a clear picture of the company's business through the years. He wanted to find out all he could about the company's operations.

The actual bookkeeping work at the company took up only part of his time. Soon Mr. Hewitt began to give him other responsible jobs to do, such as hiring workmen to make repairs on real estate properties which the company owned and collecting rents from persons occupying these properties. Immediately everybody learned that it was impossible to put anything over on young John D. Rockefeller.

During this period John had to live entirely on his savings, because he received no pay from the company while he was working on trial. For this reason he had to be as frugal as possible.

Besides keeping records at the company, he kept a personal account on the side. He spent a dime for a little red-covered notebook, which he labeled "Ledger A." Inside he kept a record of every penny he spent. His first entry was the dime that he spent to purchase the book. His second entry was a dime that he contributed to a missionary cause at the church.

Many of the entries in John's notebook were for religious-related donations. Besides these donations he contributed five cents weekly to the support of a religious newspaper. At Thanksgiving time, he bought food for needy families, even though he desperately needed a new overcoat to wear to work.

John's trial period ended the day after Christmas, but when the day came, neither Mr. Hewitt nor Mr. Tuttle mentioned it to him. Immediately he became alarmed because he fast was running out of money. He either had to be paid soon for the work he had already done or look for another job. "I'll manage somehow to get along for another week," he decided. "Then, if necessary, I'll ask for an explanation."

On the day after New Years, exactly one week

later, Mr. Hewitt called John into his office and handed him a bulky envelope containing $50.00. "Here is your pay for your work up to date," he said. "We have paid you at the rate of approximately $3.50 a week."

John took the bulky envelope containing the $50.00 in cash. He was happily surprised because he hadn't expected to receive so much. "Thank you, Mr. Hewitt," he said.

"We have been highly pleased with your work and plan to keep you," said Mr. Hewitt. "From now on we will pay you $25.00 a month."

Now John tried harder than ever to do good work. He succeeded so well that Mr. Hewitt and Mr. Tuttle began to treat him almost like a partner. They invited him to meet with them to help make decisions. Often they asked his advice and usually followed it.

John worked hard for Hewitt and Tuttle, but hoped sometime to establish a similar business of his own. Through friendly merchants he learned how to make money by buying and selling produce on the side. These dealings in no way interfered with his work at the company.

As time passed, he discovered that he could make more money from these side deals than he could by working for Hewitt and Tuttle. Some of his friends urged him to quit his regular job and go into business for himself, but he hesitated to take the chance. For one thing, he lacked the necessary funds.

Most of all, he felt obligated to Hewitt and Tuttle for giving him a start and for treating him like a partner in their business. Moreover, he liked both of them as friends. "I'll never leave them unless a special opportunity comes along," he said.

Before long, he happened to talk with a friend of his, named Maurice B. Clark, who worked for a competing company. Maurice revealed that he was eager to start a company of his own. "At present I have only $2,000 in the bank," he said, "but as soon as I can increase my savings to $4,000, I'll make the move."

By now the Rockefeller family had moved to Cleveland so that William could attend Central High School. At Christmas time, Big Bill announced that he had set aside money so each of his children would inherit $1,000.00 at the age of twenty-one. At once John tried to persuade his father to let him have his $1,000 immediately. Then, perhaps, he could form a partnership with his friend Maurice.

"I won't let you have your inheritance now," replied Big Bill, "but I'll lend you $1,000 provided you'll agree to pay me interest."

"Oh, good!" cried John excitedly. "I'll gladly pay you interest on the loan."

Immediately John hurried off to find his friend Maurice. "Would you consider taking me as a partner in your new commission merchandising company?" he asked. "You already have $2,000, and I have found that I can raise $2,000. By forming a partnership, we can get started in business at once."

Maurice accepted John's proposal, and in March, 1859, the new firm of Clark and Rockefeller opened its doors for business. Maurice Clark was only 21 years old, and John D. Rockefeller less than 20 years old, yet both were inspired with confidence that they could succeed.

From Produce to Oil

FROM THE START, Rockefeller was the financial officer of the company. He learned quickly that business could be conducted far more cheaply on a large-scale basis than on a small scale. By buying produce in carload lots, he could get better prices and lower railroad rates.

Large-scale buying of produce required large sums of money. Rockefeller solved this problem by borrowing money from the bank where they deposited the receipts from their business. Almost at once the company began to prosper.

During its first year, Clark and Rockefeller did a gross business of $450,000, which netted the young partners $4,400 or $2,200 apiece clear profit. This was more than three times as much as Rockefeller had earned at Hewitt and Tuttle the year before.

After the War between the States started in 1861, Clark and Rockefeller's business skyrocketed. The company handled many products which the United States Government needed desperately to feed the soldiers in the Northern armies. Each partner now spent most of his time doing what he could do best. Clark traveled widely in order to buy and sell produce. Rockefeller stayed in the office to manage the business, keep records, and maintain good relations with banks, credit agencies, and the like.

Everybody with whom Rockefeller dealt came to admire and respect him. He conducted business transactions both fairly and carefully. He never let sympathy interfere with doing business efficiently. Once he refused to advance money to a shipper for produce that the shipper had failed to deliver on time. "Occasionally you have to bend a little," said his partner Clark. "After all, you borrow money yourself."

"Yes, but only by giving tangible security," replied Rockefeller. "Otherwise it would be unbusinesslike to borrow."

Even though Rockefeller was careful in handling money, he wasn't the least bit miserly. He gave generously both to his church and to charities. When he was only 21 years old, he financed the building of a new home for his family. This new home was by far the finest dwelling in which the Rockefellers had ever lived.

During these years Rockefeller devoted much time and attention to the church. He taught a class at Sunday school, and even helped to sweep the floors, wash the windows, and cut grass or shovel snow, according to the season. When the church failed to pay a debt of $2,000 and was threatened with being closed, he personally undertook to raise the money. He pledged $200 himself and methodically called on other members in their homes to persuade them to pledge the balance. Within two months he managed to save the church.

For this service he was made a trustee of the church, responsible for keeping track of the financial records. In a short time he became recognized as the most influential member of the congregation. The minister respected him for his helpful efforts and often referred to him as his "right hand man."

Running a successful business and attending to the needs of his church kept Rockefeller busy seven days a week. Nevertheless, he found time to keep up on events which were happening in the world. In November, 1859, he read a report in the Cleveland *Morning Leader* that oil had been discovered near Titusville, a small town in western Pennsylvania. Already many excited outsiders were rushing to that area.

At first only a few people in Cleveland became interested in this discovery of oil. One was a former employer of Maurice Clark, now Rockefeller's partner. This early investor bought up land in western Pennsylvania and drilled a well that turned out to be a gusher.

From then on, more and more businessmen in Cleveland, including both Rockefeller and Clark, began to investigate the oil reports coming from western Pennsylvania. "We might lose out on something big unless we buy some land there," said Clark during a conference.

"Yes," replied Rockefeller, "but we might also lose our shirts." He tapped his fingers thoughtfully on the arms of his chair. "How about my making a special trip to Titusville to look into the matter?" he said.

"That's a splendid idea," said Clark. "Go and

investigate the situation thoroughly. I'll look after things here while you are away."

Rockefeller had a hard time reaching Titusville because no railroad went directly there. He had to leave a train and ride horseback for some distance in order to get there. Ordinarily he liked to ride horseback, but not when he was on urgent business.

After he reached Titusville, he explored the oil operations thoroughly. He visited areas where noisy engines were drilling new wells and other areas where engines were pumping oil from wells. He talked with many people, some of whom were so excited about oil that they were beginning to call it "black gold."

As he looked, listened, and learned, he quickly concluded that the oil business involved three separate operations: production, refining, and transportation. Production was uncertain because experts already had discovered that much land was barren of oil. Refining and transportation also were uncertain because they depended entirely on production.

When Rockefeller returned to Cleveland, he reported his findings to Clark and other young businessmen. "I recommend staying out of the oil business now," he said, "but suggest keeping an eye on it for the future."

In the fall of 1861, Rockefeller accidentally met Cettie Spelman again at a musicale. Since the days when they had taken piano lessons together at Central High School, she had attended a finishing school in the East. Now she had returned home to teach in the Cleveland schools.

After this chance meeting, Rockefeller frequently saw her at social affairs about the city. He was much pleased to learn that she was interested in religious and charitable activities. Accordingly, as a first date, he asked her to accompany him to a social gathering at his church.

From then on he dated her frequently and took her to preaching services at the church.

In the meantime he continued to watch closely the developments in the oil industry. Already several small refineries had sprung up in Cleveland. One of these refineries was operated by Samuel Andrews, who occasionally bought produce from Clark and Rockefeller. One day, when he stopped at the company to order produce, he said, "I'm getting a higher yield of kerosene from crude oil than anybody else in Cleveland. If I had more capital, I could really accomplish wonders."

This reference to kerosene caused Rockefeller to recall the time when he and his father had gone to the Moravia Hotel to see the wonderful kerosene lamps. At that time his father had predicted that sometime a fortune could be made in refining. Now Mr. Andrews seemed to be proving that this prediction was true.

"How much capital do you think you need?" asked Rockefeller cautiously.

His partner Clark gazed at him, amazed but delighted. "Would you really consider investing in an oil refinery?" he asked.

"I might," said Rockefeller.

After this conversation, Rockefeller carefully investigated the refinery business. Finally he and Clark decided to go into partnership with Andrews. Clark would work actively with Andrews, and Rockefeller would run the produce company. The new oil company would be known as Andrews, Clark, and Company.

During the coming months and years, the new company accomplished wonders just as Andrews had predicted. It prospered partly because of the growth of railroads, which simplified the problem of transportation. Railroads now provided spurs into oil fields to pick up oil.

All the while, even though Rockefeller was

ANDREWS - CLARK COMPANY

intensely busy, he found time to court Cettie Spelman. Finally on his twenty-fifth birthday, July 8, 1864, he proposed to her. "Will you marry me, Cettie?" he asked. "I feel sure that I can provide a comfortable home for you."

Cettie accepted his proposal, and a couple of months later they were married. They took a long wedding trip to Niagara Falls and on into Canada, and returned by way of New England and New York. Back in Cleveland they lived in a house near Rockefeller's parents.

In 1865 large oil fields were discovered in another section of Pennsylvania. This discovery led Rockefeller to decide that he should discontinue the produce commission business and engage actively in the oil business. A few days later, he had a short talk with Andrews. "I would like to move actively into the oil business," he said. "Do you suppose Clark would buy my interest in the commission business?"

"I hope so," replied Andrews. "Somehow he and I don't get along, and I wish he would leave. Possibly if he buys your interest in the produce commission company, he will be willing to sell his interest in the refining company."

Clark readily bought Rockefeller's interest in the produce commission company, but refused to sell his interest in the refining company. Now Andrews became all the more determined to get rid of him. Finally he decided to dissolve the refining company and put it up for sale to the highest bidder.

In February, 1865, he placed a dissolution notice in the Cleveland *Morning Leader*. This notice infuriated Clark and he and his brothers submitted a bid or financial offer to purchase the refinery. In the meantime Andrews persuaded Rockefeller to join him in submitting a bid. Together they submitted a higher bid than the Clarks and obtained possession of the plant.

On February 15, the *Morning Leader* carried the following notice of co-partnership:

> The undersigned, having purchased the entire interest of Andrews, Clark, and Company in the "Excelsior Oil Works," and all stock of barrels, oil, etc., will continue the business of the late firm under the name of Rockefeller and Andrews.
>
> John D. Rockefeller
> Samuel Andrews

"Now," Rockefeller said humorously to Andrews, "let's set about revolutionizing the oil industry, but systematically and quietly."

Mr. Standard Oil

JOHN D. ROCKEFELLER at twenty-five years of age was the same cautious individual that he had been as a child. He had carefully studied all aspects of the oil industry and had discovered that it suffered greatly from incompetence, disorder, and waste. Now that he had entered the industry, he was determined to correct some of these unfortunate conditions.

First, as head of the new company he inaugurated a policy of economy in operations. Instead of buying crude oil from middlemen, he arranged to buy it directly from wells. Instead of engaging independent companies to distribute the oil, he hired men to distribute it directly. Instead of buying barrels for storage, he began to manufacture barrels.

The next thing he did was to make arrangements to export oil to other countries. In this connection, he selected the help of his brother, William, who already had proved to be a successful salesman for another company. He set up a separate company for William in New York to be known as William Rockefeller and Company. Thus by 1867 he controlled two companies in the oil industry, the refining company and the export company.

Rockefeller now had two partners whom he knew he could trust, but he realized that he would have to take in others, if the company was to grow according to his dreams. Constantly he looked about for other men with high standards of ability and reliability.

During the coming weeks and months he discovered that the company needed additional capital in order to continue to expand. It took huge sums of money to make the changes which were necessary for more efficient operations. Much new equipment had to be purchased and new and better records had to be kept.

In 1867 Rockefeller persuaded two other wealthy men from Cleveland to join his company, Henry M. Flagler and Stephen Harkness. Both invested money in the company, with Flagler becoming an active partner and Harkness a silent partner. The reorganized company was known as Rockefeller, Flagler, and Andrews.

Much of the capital which Flagler and Harkness brought into the company was used for expansion. With larger refining facilities, the company rapidly increased its production. Within a short time it tripled its output of oil. Following this increase, it produced more barrels of oil per day than any other refinery in

Cleveland. More than that, it produced more than any other company in America.

Because of its size, the company possessed tremendous power in dealing with other companies. For instance, it was able to negotiate a contract with railroads to make quantity shipments of crude oil at a discount of 15 cents per barrel. Later some of its competitors also were able to obtain reduced shipping rates, but never to equal this amount.

Each succeeding year the company kept on prospering from business efficiency. On the one hand it continued to refine and to ship more and more barrels of oil per day. On the other hand, it continued to economize in every way possible. Rockefeller, ever remembering his mother's childhood warning, "Willful waste makes woeful want," made sure that nothing was wasted which could possibly be used.

The outstanding success of Rockefeller, Flagler, and Andrews attracted wide attention. In late 1869 two wealthy New York businessmen, Benjamin Brewster and O. B. Jennings, expressed interest in investing in the company. Their interest led Rockefeller, Flagler, and Andrews to decide to change the nature of the company from a partnership to a corporation, in which each part owner would buy shares of stock in the company. Then each person's part of the company would depend on the number of shares of stock that he purchased.

Early in January, 1870, the owners of the company held a meeting and voted to establish the new corporation. In accordance with Ohio laws, they declared themselves "a body corporate for manufacturing petroleum and dealing in petroleum and its products, operating under the name of The Standard Oil Company."

The new company was incorporated for 10,000 shares of stock worth $100 each. The following six interested persons purchased shares of stock: John D. Rockefeller, William Rockefeller, Stephen Harkness, Henry M. Flagler, Samuel Andrews and O. B. Jennings, with John D. Rockefeller purchasing more than twice as many shares as anyone else. These six shareholders, acting as a Board of Directors, elected John D. Rockefeller, President; William Rockefeller, Vice-President; Henry M. Flagler, Secretary and Treasurer.

At the time when The Standard Oil Company was incorporated, it owned two refineries, a barrel-manufacturing plant and lake shipping facilities in Cleveland. In addition, it owned warehouses and storage tanks in New York, a fleet of barges in New York harbor, warehouses with railroad sidings in the Pennsylvania oil regions, and numerous railroad tank cars.

With these holdings The Standard Oil Company was the largest oil company in America, but it controlled only about one-tenth of the refining industry in the country. Rockefeller realized that if it was to dominate the oil business, it had to control more of the refining industry. Somehow he had to find ways to purchase and absorb many small refineries that still existed in different parts of the country.

At once he set out on a methodical program of purchasing small refining firms and bringing them into the Standard Oil Company. By 1872 he had purchased 34 such rival firms by paying them off with shares of stock in the company. Now the company owned all the refineries in Cleveland and controlled about one-half of all the oil refined in the country.

Rockefeller still was unsatisfied. Now that the company had become this powerful, he wanted it to become still more powerful. From then on he strived mainly to gain control of some of the remaining large competitors.

In 1873 he purchased a large refining company in New York, which helped to establish The Standard Oil Company in the East. During the same year he purchased another refinery in Louisville, Kentucky, which helped to establish the company in the South. One year later he purchased a refinery in the heart of the oil-well region of Pennsylvania. Following these three purchases, he had very little competition left. Now at last he actually ruled over the mammoth oil empire of which he had dreamed.

During these busy years Rockefeller always took ample time from company responsibilities to devote to his family and church. He was more content to relax at home than any other place, and always looked forward to spending evenings and weekends with his family. He found time, however to attend church services regularly, even during the week. He never was too busy to help carry on worthy projects for the church.

The Rockefeller family now included three daughters. For years Rockefeller had wanted a son whom he could bring up as an heir to the oil business. Finally in 1874, just as he had succeeded in building his mammoth company, he obtained this wish with the birth of John D. Jr. He was so pleased with the arrival of this son and heir that he offered thanks to God and said, "Now my cup runneth over."

At this time Rockefeller maintained two homes for his family. One was a comfortable residence near his office in the heart of Cleveland, and the other was a country estate, called Forest Hills, some miles away along the shores of Lake Erie. His family actually lived in both these homes, spending the colder months of the year at the house in the heart of the city and the warmer months at Forest Hills.

The family especially enjoyed spending the summers at Forest Hills. Rockefeller maintained an excellent stable of riding horses where John D. Jr. and his sisters could have their own favorite horses. Besides he made it possible for them to enjoy all sorts of water sports along Lake Erie. All members of the family, however, were required to work. John D. Jr., for instance, was required to toil with the regular laborers, trimming shrubbery and mowing the lawn to help keep the estate in order.

While Rockefeller was building his oil empire, he faced many charges of using unfair practices. He was accused of being ruthless in conducting business transactions. Mostly these were situations in which he brought pressure on small competing companies in order to force them to sell. In all cases, however, he was careful to stay within the law in dealing with these companies. He continuously consulted lawyers to make certain his transactions would be safe.

The problems of managing The Standard Oil

Company were tremendous. The company now owned many different kinds of plants and had working agreements with many others. All employees had to be informed about the company policies and routines. New leaders had to be selected and trained for top-level positions in the various branches and divisions.

As President, Rockefeller attempted to keep informed on every possible detail. He required all plants and divisions to submit frequent reports. He kept a watchful eye on all purchases and expenditures to make sure they were economical, and on all sales to make sure they were profitable. He even insisted on checking and approving the employment of every worker, regardless of rank. "I think of every employee as a brick, board, or beam in this important edifice which we call The Standard Oil Company," he said. "I must be sure that he contributes some measure of strength to the total structure."

The second most powerful figure in the company was Flagler who functioned as Secretary and Treasurer. He not only kept the records but he supervised the operations in most of the divisions and plants. He was a specialist on transportation and handled most of the relations with railroads. He met regularly with Rockefeller to submit reports and to help plan company strategies.

Within a few years under this effective leadership, the Standard Oil Company developed a very efficient organization. From then on its chief problem was public opinion. Many people felt that no company had a right to dominate an industry or to become a monopoly.

In 1879 the State of Pennsylvania brought suit against the Standard Oil Company, accusing it of conspiracy to prevent competition and to control prices in the oil industry. This case was ultimately dismissed, but it clearly revealed that somehow the so-called monopoly must be broken up. From now on the company must operate as a group of smaller companies with a central office for general management.

In 1882 the company took action to dissolve and to incorporate as three separate companies, the Standard Oil Company of Ohio, the Standard Oil Company of New York, and the Standard Oil Company of Pennsylvania. Also, it made provisions to incorporate companies in other states, if and when other breakdowns became advisable. This new group of oil companies was to be known as the Standard Oil Trust, with its headquarters or home office in New York City.

A Name of Distinction

AFTER THE reorganization of the Standard Oil Company, the Standard Oil Trust erected a massive office building in the heart of New York. Under Rockefeller's leadership the company immediately began to prosper. It operated efficiently and came to control more and more of the oil business of the country. This success, however, led to renewed accusations from the public that the company was profiting unfairly from big-business operations.

When Rockefeller moved to New York, he bought a four-story brownstone mansion for his family fairly close to his office. Also, he bought an adjoining vacant lot where his children would have room to play and carry on a variety of healthful activities. Both he and his wife Cettie planned means of helping them to grow up to lead normal active lives. All were taught to know life as it really exists in the world. Each had to carry on certain chores or duties around home for the good of the others.

According to the customs of the times, the Rockefeller daughters received most of their instruction at home from their mother and private tutors. John D. Jr., however, attended regular schools. He was a good, conscientious student but not the brilliant student that his father had been. All the children received religious instruction at the church. All were required to attend church services regularly in a family group.

Of all the Rockefeller children, John D. Jr. was the closest by far to his father. After he finished high school, he entered Brown University at Providence, Rhode Island. Here he continued through four years of college under the close observation of his father. "I am looking forward and relying upon you to share my responsibilities as soon as you are ready," his father frequently reminded him.

Indirectly Rockefeller's concern over John D. Jr.'s education led him to become interested in founding a great university. In 1886, the small University of Chicago was forced to close for want of adequate funds. Subsequently Dr. Frederick T. Gates, a minister in the Baptist Education Society, attempted to raise funds to save this little institution.

Rockefeller was very much impressed with Dr. Gates, both as a religious leader and as a businessman. Together they worked out a plan whereby Rockefeller would contribute a huge amount to re-establish the university, provided others together would pledge a matching amount. The campaign ended successfully in 1892 with the full amount assured.

When the board of trustees of the new university met, it attempted to secure Dr. William Rainy Harper of Yale University as President. At first Dr. Harper refused to accept the position unless the endowment fund, or reserve fund, of the university could be increased by a million dollars. Rockefeller promptly donated this amount so that the noted educational leader could become the first President.

Soon after this important philanthropic activity was concluded, Dr. Gates became one of Rockefeller's principal financial advisers. Years later after coming to know Rockefeller intimately, he commented, "He is one of the most trustworthy men I have ever known. He never deviates one hair's breadth from the best standards of business and moral rectitude."

Through the succeeding years Rockefeller kept a watchful eye on the University of Chicago and continued to support it financially. Repeatedly he made contributions for specific purposes. Each Christmas he regularly gave the University a million dollars.

During the 1800's a new-type engine, called the internal combustion engine, was invented. This new engine obtained its power from the explosion of gas derived from gasoline. By 1900 gasoline engines had started to come into use to run small machinery and to propel automobiles, which recently had been invented.

The use of gasoline for power opened up an entirely new field for the oil industry. Up to now kerosene, which was mainly used for lighting, had been one of the industry's chief products. Now, with the possible demand for huge quantities of gasoline, the industry was on the verge of tremendous expansion.

The developing demand for gasoline led to new attacks on the Standard Oil Company. Competitors and others argued that no one company should be allowed to control the output of such an important product.

In 1896 Rockefeller decided to retire from active duties with the Standard Oil Company so that he could devote more of his time to philanthropic activities. He was less than sixty years old, but he felt that the time had come to turn over most of his business responsibilities to others. He had hoped to bring John D. Jr. into the company, but John D. Jr. still had to complete another year in college.

The second-ranking officer with the Standard Oil Company was John D. Archbold, Vice-President. When Rockefeller announced his intention to retire, Archbold begged him to retain his title as President. "You are Mr. Standard Oil," he said. "The name of John D.

Archbold doesn't mean anything in the world." In accordance with Archbold's wishes, Rockefeller kept the title of President of the company.

In 1897 John D. Jr. graduated from Brown University and quietly moved into his father's office. From the beginning he was disturbed by the constant turmoil and battling in the business world. He disliked many of Archbold's decisions, which he considered grossly unfair. Even so, he felt obliged to report to the office regularly and to try to learn as much about the business as possible. This, he realized, was what his father wanted him to do.

Around the turn of the century, Rockefeller with the help of his financial adviser, Dr. Gates, and the cooperation of several prominent physicians, established a foundation, called the Rockefeller Institute for Medical Research. The purpose of this foundation was to provide funds for the study and control of devastating diseases. Funds were made available to medical schools for clinical and laboratory research in many parts of the country. One of the first notable achievements was discovering a means of combating spinal meningitis.

At about this same time Rockefeller and Dr. Gates became interested in establishing an organization, called the General Education Board, to improve the general level of education in America. This board functioned largely by appropriating funds to colleges and universities willing to cooperate in providing suitable programs. In time it became a very powerful educational organization in America.

Some years later Rockefeller established the Rockefeller Foundation to promote the well-being of people throughout the world. Primarily this organization sought to improve health and educational conditions in remote areas. In establishing these foundations and making related gifts, Rockefeller contributed approximately five hundred million dollars.

While Rockefeller was engrossed in philanthropic activities, the Standard Oil Company and other large corporations began to have trouble with the federal government. In 1901, Theodore Roosevelt, who had been elected Vice-President in 1900, began to make speeches attacking them as menaces to the country. Nothing like this had ever happened before.

Later in 1901 an unexpected event occurred. President William H. McKinley was assassinated after making a speech in Buffalo, New York, and Roosevelt became President. Following this event, large corporations became worried about their future.

During the next few years, the federal government began actively to investigate the operations of large corporations. These investigations led to widespread attacks on big business. Rockefeller suffered wide abuse, because most people thought that he still was engaged in active management of the company.

In 1906 matters for the Standard Oil Company came to a head. The Attorney General of the United States brought suit against it for carrying on unfair business practices. This suit was in the courts for a period of five years. Finally in 1911 the Supreme Court found the company guilty by rendering the following decision: "There is but one way to treat this dangerous corporate machine. It must be broken into its original units, so that free competition in the oil business may be restored."

After this Supreme Court decision the company took action to break itself up into a parent company to be known as the Standard Oil Company of New Jersey and 34 smaller companies. Each company was to have its own board of directors and its own officers. Actually, however, this action had little effect on the methods of doing business because the same small group owned all the companies.

During this period, John D. Jr. had a serious talk with his father. He explained that he had no interest in becoming President and that he wanted to drop out of the company. His father realized that he had come to this decision after years of study and made no effort to change his mind. Instead he merely asked, "What do you plan to do with your time?"

"I simply want to help you manage our family fortune," replied John D. Jr.

After the Standard Oil Company complied with the Supreme Court decision and broke up into smaller companies, Rockefeller resigned as President, which he had been in name only. He wanted no part in the further management of the company. In recent years he had developed a variety of minor health problems, which he felt could be corrected by exercise in the fresh air. Also, he had developed baldness, which he tried to disguise by wearing a cap when he appeared in public.

For exercise he took long walks, played golf, and carried on other suitable activities. One of his greatest pleasures came from handing out shiny new dimes to children. He always seemed to have his pockets bulging with dimes to use for this purpose.

After he retired, he spent much time at Pocantico Hills, a country estate which he had purchased near Tarrytown, New York. Here he developed a passion for planting trees and actually planted a woods with special paths to be used for horseback and bicycle riding, both of which all members of the family enjoyed. Also he constructed a golf course on the property so that they could play golf at home.

John D. Jr. tried to spend as much time as

possible with his father in both work and play. When he married in 1901, he and his wife bought a home near the Rockefeller brownstone mansion downtown. Later he purchased a country estate near Pocantico Hills.

Rockefeller and Cettie were very happy to have John D. Jr. and his wife living nearby. They were especially happy when grandchildren began to arrive. The first was a granddaughter born in 1903, named Abby after her mother. Then came five grandsons born about two years apart: John D. III, Nelson A., Laurance S., Winthrop, and David.

Rockefeller always felt fortunate to have married Cettie. Once in his later life he was invited to speak at the Baptist church in Cleveland where he had taken her on their first date. She accompanied him to the church and sat in the audience to listen to his speech. At one point he looked over at her and said, "People say that I have accomplished much in my life, but my greatest accomplishment has been to win Cettie Spelman as my wife. She has given me the greatest possible happiness."

During Cettie's later years, she was virtually an invalid. Rockefeller arranged a great family reunion for her with all their children and grandchildren present. He even employed an orchestra to provide a concert of the musical selections that she enjoyed most.

When Cettie died in 1915, Rockefeller sadly missed her after many years of happy companionship. At once he took steps to honor her by establishing the Laura Spelman Memorial Foundation. The chief purpose of this foundation was to promote child welfare.

In succeeding years Rockefeller moved out of Pocantico Hills and left it to the use of his children and grandchildren. He spent most of his summers at Golf House, which was the club house on a private golf course which he purchased at Lakewood, New Jersey. At this stage, most persons who wanted to confer with him had to join him in playing a game of golf.

In later years he spent most of his winters at The Casements, an estate which he purchased near Ormond Beach, Florida. Regularly in Florida he attended the Ormond Beach Union Church. Following the church services, he enjoyed standing at the church door and shaking hands with the members leaving the church. "It's a means of showing people I'm their friend," he said.

When Rockefeller died in 1937, about six weeks before his 98th birthday, he was honored with special tributes throughout the United States and world. All the employees of the Standard Oil organization ceased work for five minutes to stand with bowed heads.

After Rockefeller's death, John D. Jr. took

over most of his father's philanthropic activities and added several of his own. Like his father, he firmly believed that money was a gift from God. It was not to be hoarded but was to be widely dispersed. Two of John D. Jr.'s leading philanthropic projects were to help restore Williamsburg, the colonial capital of Virginia, and to help build a home for the United Nations in New York City.

Following John D. Jr.'s death in 1950, his sons have proudly tried to carry on the family tradition of manifesting deep concern for the welfare of others. Each son has made a notable niche in history: John D. III as a patron of the performing arts; Nelson A. as Governor of New York; Laurance S. as a conservationist and sociologist; Winthrop as a rancher and Governor of Arkansas; and David as Chairman of the Board of Directors of Chase Manhattan Bank. All are still active except Winthrop, who died in 1973.

Today the name Rockefeller is a name of great distinction in America. When people see or hear this name, they immediately think of all the good that Rockefeller money has done and still is doing in the world. They think of the hundreds of classrooms, libraries, hospitals, clinics, laboratories, and recreational centers where Rockefeller money is actively at work for the welfare of mankind.

John D. Rockefeller had a great yen for making money, but he had an even greater urge to give it away. Without question he was both one of the shrewdest businessmen and one of the greatest benefactors of all time.

More About This Book

WHEN JOHN D. ROCKEFELLER LIVED

1839 JOHN D. ROCKEFELLER WAS BORN IN RICHFORD, NEW YORK, JULY 8.

There were twenty-six states in the Union.

Martin Van Buren was President.

The population of the country was about 15,810,000.

1839–1853 JOHNNY LIVED AND ATTENDED SCHOOL IN CENTRAL NEW YORK AND NORTHEASTERN OHIO.

Charles Goodyear discovered the process of vulcanizing rubber, 1839.

Oil was first sold commercially as Seneca oil, a patent medicine, 1841.

The United States acquired the Oregon Territory south of the 49th parallel, 1846.

The Mexican War was fought, 1846–48.

Gold was discovered in California, 1849, and California became a state, 1850.

Harriet Beecher Stowe's *Uncle Tom's Cabin* was published, 1852.

1855–1863 ROCKEFELLER BEGAN HIS BUSINESS CAREER IN THE FIELD OF PRODUCE MERCHANDISING.

The first oil company in the United States was organized, 1855.

The War between the States began, 1861.

The first transcontinental telegraph was completed, 1869.

1863–1893 ROCKEFELLER ENTERED THE OIL INDUSTRY AND FOUNDED THE STANDARD OIL COMPANY.

The War between the States ended, 1865.

Alexander Graham Bell invented the telephone, 1876.

Clara Barton founded the American Red Cross, 1881.

Thomas Edison invented the motion picture camera, 1889.

1893–1937 ROCKEFELLER RETIRED TO DEVOTE THE REST OF HIS LIFE TO PHILANTHROPY.

The Panama Canal was completed and opened to world traffic, 1914.

World War I was fought, 1914–1918.

Stock market prices crashed and a severe depression followed, 1929.

1937 JOHN D. ROCKEFELLER DIED AT HIS HOME AT ORMOND BEACH, FLORIDA, MAY 23.

There were forty-eight states in the Union.

Franklin D. Roosevelt was President.

The population of the country was about 128,680,000.

DO YOU REMEMBER?

1. Why was Johnny surprised when he saw a horse and buggy approaching the Rockefeller home?
2. How did Johnny get an opportunity to meet a real Cayuga Indian?
3. How did the Rockefeller family move comfortably from Richford to Moravia?
4. How did Johnny earn money to help the family when his father was away?
5. What did Johnny see when he visited the general store with his father?
6. How did Johnny prove that he was smarter than a turkey?
7. How did John first find out about kerosene as a means of providing light?

8. What important lesson about money did John learn one summer at Owego?
9. Why were John and William left out of the school picture at Owego Academy?
10. What interesting experiences did the Rockefellers have on their long trip to Ohio?
11. How did John enter into church and school activities in Cleveland, Ohio?
12. How did Rockefeller achieve success as a young produce commission merchant?
13. How did Rockefeller get a successful start in the oil industry?
14. How did Rockefeller manage to build the largest oil company in America?
15. Why did Rockefeller become known as one of the world's greatest philanthropists?

IT'S FUN TO LOOK UP THESE THINGS

1. Where is Cleveland, the city in which Rockefeller started his fabulous career?
2. How did most people in the early days of our country light their houses?

3. How did kerosene lamps become a very popular form of lighting houses?
4. How did invention of the internal combustion engine create a demand for gasoline?
5. What is crude oil and why must it be refined before it can be used?
6. Where are the leading oil-producing sections of the United States today?

INTERESTING THINGS YOU CAN DO

1. Collect pictures of activities in the oil industry for an exhibit on the bulletin board.
2. Prepare a report telling what takes place in an oil refinery.
3. Make a list of purposes for which different kinds of oil are used today.
4. Name other men of Rockefeller's time who became famous industrial leaders.
5. Mention a few industrial leaders besides Rockefeller who became philanthropists.
6. Explain why endowments are needed to support many educational organizations.

OTHER BOOKS YOU MAY ENJOY READING

Andrew Carnegie: Young Steelmaker, Joanne Landers Henry. Trade and School Editions, Bobbs-Merrill.

Black Gold at Titusville, Lavinia Dobler. Dodd Mead.

Great Oildorado, The, Hildegarde Dolson. Random House.

Henry Ford: Boy with Ideas, Hazel B. Aird and Catherine Ruddiman. Trade and School Editions, Bobbs-Merrill.

Oil Field Boy, Merritt Mauzey. Abelard-Schuman.

Oil, Today's Black Magic, Walter Buehr. Morrow.

INTERESTING WORDS IN THIS BOOK

accidence (ăk′sĭ dĕns): pronunciation of words, rules of grammar

accumulate (ă kū′mů lāt): acquire, amass or build up

accusation (ăk ů zā′shŭn): act of condemning

adage (ăd′ĭj): old saying, proverb

anticipate (ăn tĭs′ĭ pāt): look forward to, expect

antiquity (an′tĭk′wĭ tĭ): relic or monument of ancient times, days of long ago

arthritis (är thrī′tĭs): inflammation of the joints

auspicious (ôs pĭsh′ŭs): fortunate, prosperous

bleak (blēk): cold and cheerless

brine (brīn): extremely salty water

capital (kăp′ĭ tăl): money or other things of value

consecutively (kŏn sĕk′ū tĭv lĭ): in regular sequence or order

conservationist (kŏn′sẽr vā′shŭn ĭst): person who works to save natural resources

dissolution (dĭs′ō lū′shŭn): act of breaking up a company or other organization

drover (drō′vẽr): person who drives cattle or other domestic animals to market

elegant (ĕl′ĕ gănt): handsome, fine

expenditure (ĕks pĕn′dĭ tūr): payment of money

frugal (frōō′găl): saving, economical

futile (fū′tĭl): useless, unsuccessful

greenback (grēn′băk): paper money, so called because it was printed in green ink

grossly (grōs′lĭ): entirely, wholly

humiliated (hū mĭl′ĭ āt′ĕd): humbled, lowered in self-respect

inaugurate (ĭn ô′gū rāt) : commence, introduce

incorporate (ĭn kôr′pō rāt) : join or unite into one body, as a business organization

intrigued (ĭn trēgd′) : fascinated, interested

jackpot (jăk′pŏt) : money accumulated by good luck, as in a game

jovially (jō′vĭ ăl ĭ) : merrily, in a jolly manner

methodical (mė thŏd′ĭ kăl) : orderly, in the habit of working in an orderly way

miserly (mī′zẽr lĭ) : in a grasping, stingy manner

modify (mŏd′ĭ fī) : change

obstinate (ŏb′stĭ nĭt) : stubborn

porridge (pŏr′ĭj) : broth made of water or milk cooked with ground cereal

prophecy (prŏf′ė sĭ) : prediction of something to happen in the future

saunter (sôn′tẽr) : walk about idly

scrawny (scrôn′ĭ) : skinny, thin

shilling (shĭl′ĭng) : coin used in the early days of our country

sociologist (sō′cĭ ŏl′ȯ jĭst) : person who studies human relations and organizations

transaction (trăns ăk′ shŭn) : business deal

Childhood
OF FAMOUS AMERICANS

COLONIAL DAYS

James Oglethorpe, *Parks*
John Alden, *Burt*
John Peter Zenger, *Long*
John Smith, *Barton*
Myles Standish, *Stevenson*
Peter Stuyvesant, *Widdemer*
Pocahontas, *Seymour*
Pontiac, *Peckham*
Squanto, *Stevenson*
Virginia Dare, *Stevenson*
William Bradford, *Smith*
William Penn, *Mason*

STRUGGLE for INDEPENDENCE

Anthony Wayne, *Stevenson*
Ben Franklin, *Stevenson*
Betsy Ross, *Weil*
Crispus Attucks, *Millender*
Dan Morgan, *Bryant*
Ethan Allen, *Winders*
Francis Marion, *Steele*
George Rogers Clark, *Wilkie*
George Washington, *Stevenson*
Israel Putnam, *Stevenson*
John Hancock, *Cleven*
John Paul Jones, *Snow*
Martha Washington, *Wagoner*
Molly Pitcher, *Stevenson*
Nathan Hale, *Stevenson*
Nathanael Greene, *Peckham*
Patrick Henry, *Barton*
Paul Revere, *Stevenson*
Tom Jefferson, *Monsell*

EARLY NATIONAL GROWTH

Abigail Adams, *Wagoner*
Alec Hamilton, *Higgins*
Andy Jackson, *Stevenson*
Black Hawk, *Cleven*
Dan Webster, *Smith*
DeWitt Clinton, *Widdemer*
Dolly Madison, *Monsell*
Eli Whitney, *Snow*
Elias Howe, *Corcoran*
Francis Scott Key, *Stevenson*
Henry Clay, *Monsell*
James Fenimore Cooper, *Winders*
James Monroe, *Widdemer*
John Audubon, *Mason*
John Fitch, *Stevenson*
John Jacob Astor, *Anderson*
John Marshall, *Monsell*
John Quincy Adams, *Weil*
Lucretia Mott, *Burnett*
Matthew Calbraith Perry, *Scharbach*
Nancy Hanks, *Stevenson*
Noah Webster, *Higgins*
Oliver Hazard Perry, *Long*
Osceola, *Clark*
Rachel Jackson, *Govan*
Robert Fulton, *Henry*
Samuel Morse, *Snow*
Sequoyah, *Snow*
Stephen Decatur, *Smith*
Stephen Foster, *Higgins*
Washington Irving, *Widdemer*
Zack Taylor, *Wilkie*

WESTWARD MOVEMENT

Brigham Young, *Jordan and Frisbee*
Buffalo Bill, *Stevenson*
Daniel Boone, *Stevenson*
Davy Crockett, *Parks*
Gail Borden, *Paradis*
Jed Smith, *Burt*
Jessie Fremont, *Wagoner*
Jim Bowie, *Winders*
Jim Bridger, *Winders*
Kit Carson, *Stevenson*
Lotta Crabtree, *Place*
Meriwether Lewis, *Bebenroth*
Narcissa Whitman, *Warner*
Sacagawea, *Seymour*
Sam Houston, *Stevenson*
Simon Kenton, *Wilkie*
Tecumseh, *Stevenson*

WILL CLARK, *Wilkie*
WILLIAM FARGO, *Wilkie*
WILLIAM HENRY HARRISON, *Peckham*
ZEB PIKE, *Stevenson*

THE NATION DIVIDED

ABE LINCOLN, *Stevenson*
ABNER DOUBLEDAY, *Dunham*
BEDFORD FORREST, *Parks*
CLARA BARTON, *Stevenson*
DAVID FARRAGUT, *Long*
HARRIET BEECHER STOWE, *Widdemer*
JEB STUART, *Winders*
JEFF DAVIS, *de Grummond and Delaune*
JULIA WARD HOWE, *Wagoner*
MARY TODD LINCOLN, *Wilkie*
RAPHAEL SEMMES, *Snow*
ROBERT E. LEE, *Monsell*
TOM JACKSON, *Monsell*
U. S. GRANT, *Stevenson*

RECONSTRUCTION and EXPANSION

ALECK BELL, *Widdemer*
ALLAN PINKERTON, *Borland and Speicher*
ANDREW CARNEGIE, *Henry*
BOOKER T. WASHINGTON, *Stevenson*
CYRUS MCCORMICK, *Dobler*
DOROTHEA DIX, *Melin*
EUGENE FIELD, *Borland and Speicher*
FRANCES WILLARD, *Mason*
GEORGE CUSTER, *Stevenson*
GEORGE PULLMAN, *Myers*
JOEL CHANDLER HARRIS, *Weddle*
JOHN DEERE, *Bare*
JOHN WANAMAKER, *Burt*
LEW WALLACE, *Schaaf*
LOUISA ALCOTT, *Wagoner*
LUTHER BURBANK, *Burt*
MARIA MITCHELL, *Melin*
MARK TWAIN, *Mason*
MARY MAPES DODGE, *Mason*
P. T. BARNUM, *Stevenson*
SITTING BULL, *Stevenson*
SUSAN ANTHONY, *Monsell*
TOM EDISON, *Guthridge*

TURN of the CENTURY

ANNIE OAKLEY, *Wilson*
DAN BEARD, *Mason*
ELIZABETH BLACKWELL, *Henry*
F. W. WOOLWORTH, *Myers*
GEORGE CARVER, *Stevenson*
GEORGE DEWEY, *Long*
GEORGE EASTMAN, *Henry*
GEORGE WESTINGHOUSE, *Dunham*
J. STERLING MORTON, *Moore*
JAMES WHITCOMB RILEY, *Mitchell*
JANE ADDAMS, *Wagoner*
JOHN BURROUGHS, *Frisbee*
JOHN PHILIP SOUSA, *Weil*
JULIETTE LOW, *Higgins*
KATE DOUGLAS WIGGIN, *Mason*
KATHARINE LEE BATES, *Myers*
LILIUOKALANI, *Newman*
THE RINGLING BROTHERS, *Burt*
ROBERT PEARY, *Clark*
TEDDY ROOSEVELT, *Parks*
WALTER REED, *Higgins*
WILBUR AND ORVILLE WRIGHT, *Stevenson*
WILL AND CHARLIE MAYO, *Hammontree*

IN RECENT YEARS

ALBERT EINSTEIN, *Hammontree*
AMELIA EARHART, *Howe*
A. P. GIANNINI, *Hammontree*
BABE DIDRIKSON, *de Grummond and Delaune*
BABE RUTH, *Van Riper, Jr.*
CARL BEN EIELSON, *Myers and Burnett*
CECIL B. DEMILLE, *Myers and Burnett*
DOUGLAS MACARTHUR, *Long*
ELEANOR ROOSEVELT, *Weil*
ERNIE PYLE, *Wilson*
ETHEL BARRYMORE, *Newman*
FRANKLIN ROOSEVELT, *Weil*
GEORGE GERSHWIN, *Bryant*
HENRY FORD, *Aird and Ruddiman*
HERBERT HOOVER, *Comfort*
JIM THORPE, *Van Riper, Jr.*
JOHN F. KENNEDY, *Frisbee*
KNUTE ROCKNE, *Van Riper, Jr.*
LEE DEFOREST, *Dobler*
LOU GEHRIG, *Van Riper, Jr.*
OLIVER WENDELL HOLMES, JR., *Dunham*
RICHARD BYRD, *Van Riper, Jr.*
ROBERT GODDARD, *Moore*
VILHJALMUR STEFANSSON, *Myers and Burnett*
WALTER CHRYSLER, *Weddle*
WILL ROGERS, *Van Riper, Jr.*
WOODROW WILSON, *Monsell*